THE
NEW
GUEST - ROOM BOOK

Assembled by F. J. Sheed

Illustrated by Enrico Arno

SHEED & WARD

London

FIRST PUBLISHED 1958
BY SHEED AND WARD LTD.
33 MAIDEN LANE
LONDON W.C.2

PRINTED IN GREAT BRITAIN BY
LOWE AND BRYDONE (PRINTERS) LTD., LONDON, N.W.10

ASSEMBLER'S NOTE

A guest-room without a book is a way of saying that your guests can't read. They will not be pleased.

But tastes vary and you can't instal a library. You want one book for every possible taste. You want this book.

Nobody will like everything in it, nobody except me, that is. But there's nothing in it that won't interest somebody. And there's nobody that won't find something in it to fill the gap between closing his door for the night and closing his eyes for the night. Though if he chooses the ghost story he may not close them for several nights.

F. J. S.

ACKNOWLEDGMENTS

I gratefully acknowledge the kindness of all those named hereunder in granting me permission to use copyright material in this anthology:

The Proprietors of *Punch* for "Take Me in Your Arms, Miss Money-penny-Wilson", by Patrick Barrington. Reproduced by permission of *Punch*.

Messrs. Gerald Duckworth & Co. Ltd., for "Ballade of Unsuccessful Men" and "The Fire", from *Sonnets and Verse*, by Hilaire Belloc.

Messrs. Cassell & Co. Ltd., for the essay "On Euphemism", from *The Silence of the Sea*, by Hilaire Belloc.

Victor Gollancz, Ltd., for the excerpt from *Journey Into a Fog*, by Margareta Berger-Hamerschlag.

Miss Dorothy Collins for extracts of prose and poetry reprinted from *Return to Chesterton*, by Maisie Ward: also for extracts of prose and poetry from the works of Chesterton *The Common Man, What's Wrong with the World, The Coloured Lands, Collected Poems, The Flying Inn, Autobiography, A Handful of Authors* and *Greybeards at Play*.

Messrs. Methuen & Co. Ltd., for the extracts from *The Flying Inn* and *Collected Poems* of G. K. Chesterton.

Messrs. Hutchinson & Co. Ltd., for the extracts from *Autobiography*.

Messrs. Faber & Faber, Ltd., for the excerpt from *The Waste Land*, by T. S. Eliot.

Messrs. William Collins, Sons & Co. Ltd., for the extract from *St. Thomas More*, by John Farrow.

Sir Alan Herbert the Proprietors of *Punch* and Ernest Benn, Ltd., for the poem "I Like Them Fluffy", from *A Book of Ballads*.

Mr. Paul Horgan for "The Surgeon and the Nun", copyright 1936 by Paul Horgan.

Mr. Evelyn Waugh for the excerpts from *The Gospel in Slow Motion* and *Literary Distractions* by Mgr. R. A. Knox.

Messrs. Burns, Oates and Washbourne Ltd., for the excerpt from *Shane Leslie's Ghost Book*.

Sister Maris Stella for "Christmas Carol for the Dog", from *Frost for St. Brigid*.

Mr. Alfred Noyes for "Daddy Fell Into the Pond", from *Daddy Fell into the Pond*, and the excerpt from *Two Worlds for Memory*.

Messrs. Macmillan & Co. Ltd., and Mrs. Stephens for "Nora Criona", from *The Hill of Vision* by James Stephens.

Dom Hubert van Zeller, O.S.B., for the excerpt from *Willingly to School*.

CONTENTS

PART I

OF MARRIAGE AND OTHER MATTERS NOT EXCLUDING LOVE

7

PART II

OF CHILDHOOD AND UNRELATED TOPICS

10

PART ONE

Of Marriage And Other Matters

Not Excluding Love

NOT EVEN SUICIDE?

ROBERT LOUIS STEVENSON

Once you are married there is nothing left for you, not even suicide, but to be good.

READ ON

J. B. MORTON

"You vixen!"

Lance Merriweather's words seemed to stop her heart beating. Was this brutal cad the man she had married? Did she love him? Had she ever loved him?

Why had she married him? What was she to do? Why had she not foreseen this? Where was the remedy? Could she endure any more? What did it mean? Who was he? How had it happened? Could this be he? When did it begin? What was it he had said? Why had she answered? What was the use of going on? Was there nothing left? Had there ever been anything? What was it all about? What did he mean? How could she know? Was there anything to know? What was love? How would it all end?

—From *The Misadventures of Dr. Strabismus.*

Read on, indeed.

13

LITTLE
MARY CASSIDY

FRANCIS A. FAHY

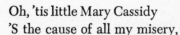

Oh, 'tis little Mary Cassidy
    'S the cause of all my misery,
The raison that I am not now the boy I used to be;
Oh, she bates the beauties all that we read about in history,
Sure half the country-side's as lost for her as me.
    Travel Ireland up and down,
    Hill, village, vale and town,
Girl like Colleen dhoun[1] you'll be looking for in vain:
    Oh, I'd rather live in poverty
    With little Mary Cassidy
Than Emperor without her be o'er Germany or Spain.

'Twas at the dance at Darmody's that first I caught a sight
        of her,
And heard her sing an Irish song till tears came in my eyes;
And ever since the blessed hour I'm dreaming day and night
        of her,
The div'l a wink of sleep I get from bed to rise.

[1] Brown-haired girl.

14

Her cheek the rose in June,
Her song the lark in tune;
Working, resting, night or noon, she never laves my mind;
Oh, till singing by my cabin fire sits little Mary Cassidy,
'Tis little aise or happiness I'm sure I'll ever find.

What is wealth or what is fame, or what is all that people fight
about,
To the kindness of her kisses, or the glancing of her eye?
Oh, though troubles throng my breast, sure they'd soon go to
the right about,
If I thought her curly head would nestle there, by'n-bye.
Take all I own today,
Kith, kin, and care away,
Ship them all across the say, or to the frozen zone,
Lave me here an orphan bare, but oh, lave me Mary Cassidy,
I never would feel lonesome with the two of us alone.

TWO STUBBORN PIECES OF IRON

G. K. CHESTERTON

In discussing such a proposal as that of the co-education of the sexes
it is very desirable first of all to realise clearly what it is that we want
the thing to do. The thing might be upheld for quite opposite reasons.
It might be supposed to increase delicacy or to decrease it. It might
be valued because it was a sphere for sentiment or because it was a
damper for sentiment. My sympathies would move me in a discussion
entirely according to what difference its upholders thought it would
make. For myself, I doubt whether it would make much difference at

all. Everyone must agree with co-education for very young children; and I cannot believe that even for elder children it would do any great harm. But that is because I think the school is not so important as people think it nowadays. The home is the really important thing, and always will be. People talk about the poor neglecting their children; but a little boy in the street has more traces of having been brought up by his mother than of having been taught ethics and geography by a pupil teacher. And if we take this true parallel of the home we can see, I think, exactly what co-education can do and what it cannot do. The school will never make boys and girls ordinary comrades. The home does not make them that. The sexes can work together in a school-room just as they can breakfast together in a breakfast-room; but neither makes any difference to the fact that the boys go off to a boyish companionship which the girls would think disgusting, while the girls go off to a girl companionship which the boys would think literally insane. Co-educate as much as you like, there will always be a wall between the sexes until love or lust breaks it down. Your co-educative playground for pupils in their teens will not be a place of sexless camaraderie. It will be a place where boys go about in fives sulkily growling at the girls, and where the girls go about in twos turning up their noses at the boys.

Now if you accept this state of things and are content with it as the result of your co-education, I am with you; I accept it as one of the mystical first facts of Nature. I accept it somewhat in the spirit of Carlyle when somebody told him that Harriet Martineau had "accepted the Universe," and he said, "By God, she'd better." But if you have any idea that co-education would do more than parade the sexes in front of each other twice a day, if you think it would destroy their deep ignorance of each other or start them on a basis of rational understanding, then I say first that this will never happen, and second that I (for one) should be horribly annoyed if it did.

I can reach my meaning best by another route. Very few people ever state properly the strong argument in favour of marrying for love or against marrying for money. The argument is not that all lovers are heroes and heroines, nor is it that all dukes are profligates or all millionaires cads. The argument is this, that the differences between a man and a woman are at the best so obstinate and exasperating that they practically cannot be got over unless there is an atmosphere of exaggerated tenderness and mutual interest. To put the matter in one metaphor, the sexes are two stubborn pieces of iron; if they are to be welded together, it must be while they are red-hot. Every woman has to find out that her husband is a selfish beast, because every man is a selfish beast by the standard of a woman. But let her find out the beast while they are both still in the story of "Beauty and the Beast." Every man has to find out that his wife is cross—that is to say, sensitive to the point of madness: for every woman is mad by the masculine standard. But let him find out that she is mad while her madness is more worth considering than anyone else's sanity.

This is not a digression. The whole value of the normal relations of man and woman lies in the fact that they first begin really to criticise each other when they first begin really to admire each other. And a good thing, too. I say, with a full sense of the responsibility of the statement, that it is better that the sexes should misunderstand each other until they marry. It is better that they should not have the knowledge until they have the reverence and the charity. We want no premature and puppyish "knowing all about girls." We do not want the highest mysteries of a Divine distinction to be understood before they are desired, and handled before they are understood. That which Mr. Shaw calls the Life Force, but for which Christianity has more philosophical terms, has created this early division of tastes and habits for that romantic purpose, which is also the most practical of all purposes. Those whom God has sundered, shall no man join.

It is, therefore, a question of what are really the co-educators' aims. If they have small aims, some convenience in organisation, some slight improvement in manners, they know more about such things than I. But if they have large aims, I am against them.

—From *The Common Man.*

HONEYMOON

G. K. CHESTERTON

Between the perfect marriage day
   And that fierce future, proud and furled,
I only stole six days,—six days,
   Enough for God to make the world.

For us is a creation made
   New moon by night, new sun by day,
That ancient elm that holds the heavens
   Sprang to its stature yesterday—
      . . . . . .

Dearest and first of all things free,
   Alone as bride and queen and friend,
Brute facts may come and bitter truths,
   But here all doubts shall have an end.
      . . . . . .

Never again with cloudy talk
   Shall life be tricked or faith undone,
The world is many and is mad,
   But we are sane and we are one.

         —From *Return to Chesterton.*

ISLAND LOVE-SONG

ROBERT FARREN

Thou'rt my sleeping,
thou'rt my waking,
my lips' breathing,
my drought's slaking.
Thou art all my treasure thou.

Thou'rt my seeing,
mine ears' hearing,
thou'rt my healing,
my heart's cheering.
Thou art all my treasure thou.

Thy lips' drowsing
mine eyes' brightness,
my soul's rousing
thy hand's lightness.
Thou art all my treasure thou.

Thou'rt my flushing,
thou'rt my paling,
my foot's rushing,
my step's failing.
Thou art all my treasure thou.

Isle my love's tide
sea-surroundeth,
new-wed bride
my heart's love crowneth.
Thou art all my treasure thou.

—From *Selected Poems*.

JEANMAIRE, JEANMAIRE!

LUCILE HASLEY

Jeanmaire, the French premiere ballerina, recently enriched my news-paper reading by consenting—in a Hollywood press interview—to give her views on American wives. I would like to quote, if you can bear it, one of the more fascinating paragraphs:

" 'I think life here in America is easier for women because they are more spoiled,' Jeanmaire said, after a thoughtful pause. 'I don't say they deserve it, but they get so much attention from their husbands.' "

After a thoughtful pause on *my* part, I hauled out my typewriter. "Jeanmaire, Jeanmaire!" I said to myself, as I settled down at the key-board. "I got some news for you, honey."

To begin with, Jeanmaire, I think you should know that Indiana (which is one of the forty-eight states and legally recognized as part of America) was settled by strong pioneer stock—from which I spring —and that the womenfolk underwent great hardships. Toiling slowly across the flat open plains in ox-pulled covered wagons—dodging the Indians—depending on wild game and fish for sustenance—cooking over open kettles—fighting off buzzards with only their sunbonnets—

It was a hard life, Jeanmaire, and I want you to know that things out here in Indiana haven't improved too much. For instance, my husband —and you'll be hearing more about *him* shortly—still feels the need to supplement our food supply by fishing. You'll also, shortly, be hearing more about *that*. Anyway, I could put up with this rude primitive existence, as what real woman couldn't, if only my husband still loved me and showered me with little attentions. Something more, you know, than just bringing home bluegills and an occasional bullhead.

My first intimation, Jeanmaire, that my husband—after sixteen years of married life—was no longer madly in love with me, came in the summer of '51. We were at Lake Wawasee and I remember the scene perfectly. We were out on the lake; the sun was just sinking; the water lapped gently against the rowboat.

"This is the end!" said my husband, as he jabbed a fat juicy catalpa worm, that squirted in all directions, onto my fishing hook. "Sixteen years of this is enough! Starting as from now on, Sister, you're going to bait your own hook."

I paled. "You can't do this to me," I said, in a husky voice. "I'll fight you, I'll fight you in every court in the land. I'll carry this thing to the Supreme Court if necessary. I'll. . . ."

He handed me my pole. "You wouldn't have a chance," he said. "Pah, a grown woman who won't bait her own hook! Why, there isn't a judge in the country who wouldn't uphold me. I'll bet they'd even award me the children without so much as—Hey! *Don't* throw your line right on top of mine. Throw it out on the other side."

So. *Now* he didn't even want me on his side of the boat, our fishing lines intimately tangled together. This was what came, I thought—as I crouched, brooding and sullen, over my pole—of trying to be a Good Sport and pretending to share my husband's passion for fishing. Why, only three weeks before (unfortunately, Jeanmaire, college professors get long summer vacations), I'd found myself in the wilds of Canada . . . being a Good Sport in a 2×4 cabin with a kerosene lamp and outdoor plumbing . . . while it rained for three solid days. And for why? To catch fish. To provide sustenance.

Oh, sure, I'd heard some people refer to fishing as a "sport" and as "recreation" but I'd never put any stock in the report. Surely, men were only driven to fishing because of sheer hunger? Nor did I put any stock in that highly suspicious endorsement of fishing that was attributed to Allah: "Allah does not deduct from the allotted time of man those hours spent in fishing." It was certainly shortening *my* life span and I felt that Allah . . .

"For heaven's sake," said my husband, interrupting my Mohammedan meditations, "*why* don't you ever check your bait?"

I gave a little jump. "Oh, I'm sure it's fine," I said nervously. The catalpa worm had probably dissolved long ago but who was I to hasten the evil hour when I'd have to replace it? "Look," I went on, to divert him, "isn't the sunset pretty now? I mean, all that purple and pink. . . ."

"Look at your bait!" he roared, sounding like Captain Queeg in *The Caine Mutiny*. "Don't you *want* to catch a fish?"

And have it eat up the worm? Don't be silly, I thought. Besides, catching a fish might now be dangerous on other grounds. Now that my husband nc longer loved me, the next edict would probably be that I even had to—oh, he couldn't, he *couldn't*. What man, with even a shred of chivalry, would expect a woman to remove the hook from the bloody and mutilated jaws of a flapping fish? No man. Except possibly my husband?

I quelled the mutiny rising in my bosom long enough to take a quick look at the worm. Something resembling about an inch of white slimy sewing thread, #60, still remained. I plopped it quickly back in the water and reported, cheerily, that the worm was in fine condition. Practically as good as new, no sense in wasting. . . .

"I saw it!" roared Captain Queeg. "Pull in that line! Now, what do you want to try putting on? A night crawler, a grub worm, or a catalpa?"

(Jeanmaire, I would like to repeat that I come from pioneer stock. I can, without batting an eyelash, kill spiders, cockroaches, June bugs, and centipedes. I once, at a snake farm outside of Washington, even stroked a drugged boa constrictor. I just can't stand *worms*, is all.)

"What," I now said in a faint voice, "is the skinniest thing you have? What has—urp—the fewest insides to ooze out?"

He handed me a six-inch slimy night crawler, and one look at it and you'd know why it crawled at *night*, that immediately slithered around my index finger and fell to the bottom of the boat. I could see it, between the boards, sluicing around in a half inch of dirty water. Drowning, I hoped.

"Rescue it," ordered Captain Queeg sternly. "We don't waste worms aboard this boat. Besides, you didn't even *try* to hang onto it."

Beads of sweat were standing out on my brow by the time I once again had the worm in starting position. "Now, don't act as if you were threading a needle," said this stranger in the boat with me. (Twenty-

22

four hours earlier he had been a kind and loving husband. Now, I felt, he would stop at nothing.) "Insert the hook firmly— No!—not in the middle, near the end—all right, now!—slide the worm onto the hook —then in and out—that's it—keep pushing. So what if part of him *has* fallen off. You've still got a good four inches to work with—keep pushing—"

"I think it's dead by now," I said, after several centuries had glided by. "Can I quit? Can we go home now?"

For answer, Queeg picked up the tin of worms, gave it a knowing thump with his hand, and extracted a fresh one.

Three night crawlers, two catalpa worms, and one grub worm later (the grub having proved the winning number), I had baited a hook to suit Queeg. That is, the worm—although badly mangled—was still alive and was, all things considered, in much better shape than I. *I*— that spoiled American wife, smothered under with attentions from my husband—barely had the strength to lean over the boat and rinse the greenish-white entrails off my hands.

Jeanmaire, I had—in the past half hour—come close (or as close as I ever would come) to what is referred to as the Dark Night of the Soul. The stark stripping of the senses—the conviction of utter abandonment by both God and man—the yearning for death. Generally, I know, a soul so tested has *already* been raised to a rare degree of sanctity but— don't be too fast, Jeanmaire, in ruling me out. I'd been married, remember, for sixteen years to you-know-who.

Besides, God's ways are inscrutable. He can, in the acid testing of the spirit, use either worms or nails. And I humbly think that I, with my very first night crawler, shot through the purgative stage like Halley's comet. That I slowly emerged into the illuminative stage when I realized, on facing the catalpa, that *my* will no longer counted. That I soared into the unitive stage when I—abandoned, in darkness, with the grub worm—still did not openly rebel against God. God, who had *invented* worms.

I just rebelled, is all, against my husband. (A human being, acting like a worm, is even more despicable than the real article.) Anyway,

Jeanmaire, I want you to know that I haven't baited a hook since that dark and dreadful scene at Wawasee. Translated, this means that I haven't gone fishing since. *This*, translated, means that this past summer—and high time, too—I took off on a two weeks' solo vacation: a vacation that is openly referred to, in these parts, as The Mrs. Hasley Mutiny.

But *you* understand, don't you, Jeanmaire? I mean, after all I'd gone through? How my old pioneer bones needed the healing rays of the sun on the Maryland seashore? How I needed, to restore my spirit, to be with kind and loving friends?

My husband, of course, stayed home and took care of the three children. But don't get any ideas, Jeanmaire, that he was *spoiling* me. I admit it was quite decent of him and all that, but—and this makes all the difference, as any woman knows—he didn't think of it *all by himself*. I had to suggest it.

"It may be true," I said, in a darkly suggestive voice, "that the family that prays together, stays together, but as for the family that *fishes* together—well, it just might work vice versa. You know what I mean?"

Queeg seemed to know.

"And before I die," I went on, in a voice that implied it wouldn't be long, "I'd like a vacation that's a *housewife's* idea of a vacation. I would like to stay in a swishy hotel and wallow in luxury. I would like to be as unpioneerish as possible. I would like, above all, to be a Poor Sport for two solid weeks and have nothing whatsoever to do with fish. Except, maybe, with a fork."

Well, Jeanmaire, it was a lovely vacation. I flew to New York and spent a week with kind and loving friends in Scarsdale, roughing it on a wooded estate that resembled Hyde Park. The only hardship I faced in Scarsdale was in having to carry my own tray out to the terrace one evening for a buffet supper. But what could I do, Jeanmaire? I mean, the hostess was my dearest friend and I could scarcely refuse—even though it meant hiking from the kitchen through the butler's pantry through the dining room, living room, and television room *before* reaching the terrace. The living room, of course, was the worst stretch. All *it* needed, it was so long, was some bowling pins at one end.

Exhausted by all this hiking, I rather dreaded—to tell the truth—the long trek to the seashore but it wasn't so bad. At least, it wasn't so bad as the ox-pulled covered wagon treks of my ancestors. You see, Jeanmaire, my friends and I flew down to Maryland in the company's private plane: complete with picture windows, swivel chairs, a lounge, and a telephone. So, having taken my usual Dramamine pill before flying, I was in fairly good condition when we reached the Colonial Hotel (which couldn't have been *more* colonial unless it had the Potomac flowing by instead of the boardwalk) and quite ready for the rigorous week ahead. Such as sauntering down to the dining room every morning and picking up a menu with *"Good morning!"* embossed on the cover. (*So* like home.) And then, after stowing away a five course breakfast, calling out to the beach boy to please—and step fast, boy!—set up our striped umbrellas and chairs for the day's lolling on the beach.

The only disturbing note, in this paradise enow, was the news from home. My husband was now, it seemed, maltreating our daughters. "I've been taking them fishing every night out at the Notre Dame lake," he wrote. "You should see them bait their own hooks by now. *They're* really good sports."

Resolutely ignoring this subtle jibe, I proceeded—after, that is, I'd dropped into the Star-of-the-Sea church to pray for my daughters—to enjoy my Poor Sport vacation with even more vigor. That is, lolling a little harder. I even, Jeanmaire, began to take a rather strange delight in the occasional fishy smell that came in on the evening sea breezes. It was a cozy live-and-let-live feeling, knowing the fish were safe and happy in their proper element and I in mine.

And then, Jeanmaire, it happened. We were lolling on the beach, one fine afternoon, when my dear friend's husband suddenly reared up on one elbow. "Hey, look!" he cried, his face and voice positively aglow. "Here comes a marlin boat! Three blue flags and one red. That means they've got three marlins aboard, Lu, and someone has earned a Good Sport medal."

26

"What d'ya mean, Good Sport medal?" I said, with a faint flicker of interest or, maybe, just because I was sensitive on the point.

"You get this little medal, see, if you catch a marlin and are good enough sport to throw it back in the sea. Come on," he said, dragging us to our feet, "let's go down and watch them land."

By the time we got there, the three marlins were strung up on exhibition although the three Poor Sports, the cads who insisted on keeping their haul, had understandably slunk away. I gazed at the eight-foot, sword-nosed, aluminum-skinned marlins with a speculative eye. What, I asked myself, would I ever want with a marlin? What could be *less* painful than to part with the creature, heave it right overboard again? Ergo, what *easier* way could I possibly find to redeem myself, in my husband's eyes, and be hailed as a Good Sport?

For the first time in my life, Jeanmaire, I felt a burning urge to go fishing. There was just one thing that bothered me. "Would the man," I asked, "bait the hook for me?"

"*Certainly!*" was the answer. "In fact, he'd insist on it. Of course, Lu, it costs seventy-five dollars to hire the yacht."

The price seemed negligible—a mere pittance, in fact, to pay the nice man for baiting my hook—and look what I'd have! A little medal. Surely, I reasoned, my husband would be only too happy to wire me the necessary money.

Jeanmaire, I know you'll find this hard to believe—even after all I've told you about Queeg—but he flatly refused to send me a penny. He wasn't, he said, paying any seventy-five dollars so I could throw a fish overboard.

So now you know, Jeanmaire. I mean, how American husbands really treat their wives and how—when it comes to a seventy-five dollar showdown—you can't say much for their sportsmanship, either.

—From *The Mousehunter.*

HOW HAPPY COULD I BE WITH EITHER

JOHN GAY

How happy could I be with either,
Were t'other dear charmer away!
But while ye thus tease me together,
To neither a word will I say.

—*Beggars' Opera.*

HOW HAPPY COULD I BE WITH BOTH°

PATRICK BARRINGTON

Take me in your arms, Miss Moneypenny-Wilson,
    Take me in your arms, Miss Bates;
Fatal are your charms, Miss Moneypenny-Wilson,
    Fatal are your charms, Miss Bates;
Say you are my own, Miss Moneypenny-Wilson,
    Say you are my own, Miss Bates;
You I love alone, Miss Moneypenny-Wilson,
    You, and you alone, Miss Bates.

Sweet is the morn, Miss Moneypenny-Wilson;
    Sweet is the dawn, Miss B.,
But sweeter than the dawn and the daisies on the lawn
    Are you, sweet nymphs, to me.

° Title not provided by author.

Sweet, sweet, sweet is the sugar to the beet,
   Sweet is the honey to the bee.
But sweeter far than such sweets are
   Are your sweet names to me.
Oh bitter, bitter, bitter is the lemon to the fritter,
   Bitter is the salt to the sea,
And bitter, very bitter was my figure to the fitter,
   Who fitted this suit on me;
Bitter to the sitter, when the crowds come and titter,
   Must the R.A.'s portrait be,
But bitterer by far than these bitternesses are
   Is your bitter, bitter scorn to me.

Moon of my delight, Miss Moneypenny-Wilson,
   Moon of my delight, Miss Bates;
Cold as you are bright, Miss Moneypenny-Wilson,
   Icily polite, Miss Bates;
Hear you not my voice, Miss Moneypenny-Wilson?
   Hear you not my voice, Miss Bates?
Are you deaf by choice, Miss Moneypenny-Wilson?
   Are you deaf by choice, Miss Bates?
Deaf to my cries, Miss Moneypenny-Wilson,
   Deaf to my sighs, Miss B.;
Deaf to my songs and the story of my wrongs,
   Deaf to my minstrelsy;
Deafer than a newt to the sound of the flute,
   Deafer than a stone to the sea;
Deafer than a heifer to the sighing of a zephyr
   Are your deaf ears to me.
Cold, cold, cold as the melancholy mould,
   Cold as the foam-cold sea,
Colder than the shoulder of a neolithic boulder
   Are the shoulders you show to me.

Cruel, cruel cruel is the flame to the fuel,
   Cruel is the axe to the tree,
But crueller and keener than a coster's concertina
   Is your cruel, cruel scorn to me.

—From *Punch*.

THE TWO WIVES OF THOMAS MORE

JOHN FARROW

A great influence in More's life at this time was provided by the holy men of the Carthusian Order, still in possession of their celebrated London Charterhouse. Here, in buildings founded by an illustrious Crusader, the white-clad monks led a solitary and contemplative existence, regulated by lengthy devotions, studies, and hard manual labour. Stout adherence to stern rule was then, as now, characteristic of an Order which in its long history has never experienced the need for reform. To those austere men, More brought his perplexities, asking them to assist in the scrutiny of his conscience. Should he take the vows and wear the cowl of their Order? Should he be simple priest or Franciscan friar? Or was it his destiny that he should remain a layman? They gave a wise decision. Thomas More was to come and live with the monks, but he was not to take vows. Time and prayer and contemplation would furnish the answer to his problems, but until he was sure of that answer, he was not to sever relations with temporal responsibilities.

More went to the Charterhouse with high purpose and strong resolve and, as far as his studies would permit, he steadfastly lived as an ordinary monk. He was given a pallet in a solitary cell and he wore a hair shirt to "tame his flesh." He observed the rules of silence and of fasting, for the monks ate but twice a day and then sparingly and without meat. He rose early in the morning to attend long devotions. There were fixed hours of prayer all through the day, and near midnight he left his cell again to assist in the singing of Matins and Lauds of the Dead. Every night and in darkness, save for the flicker of the sanctuary light and a few oil lamps, the monks chanted for nearly three hours. It was an impressive, but surely a melancholy, exercise, for the monks sang with a dolorous note. "As the duty of a good monk is rather to lament than to sing," say the rubrics, "we must so sing that lamentation, not the joy of singing, be in our hearts."

For nearly three years Thomas More remained with the Carthusian Order, then of a sudden he left the Charterhouse and wholeheartedly gave his attention to public affairs and the practice of Law. The sixteenth century was but three years old when this quick departure from the cloister occurred, and the two years following saw More established as a barrister, elected to Parliament, and married to a country miss from Essex.

What occasioned this abrupt change of thought and action? The question of priest, monk, or layman had been solved in favour of the last, but certainly not because of loss of faith. More remained deeply religious, even to the degree of continuing to subject himself to the penance of the hair shirt. The decision could not have been born of mere whim or impulse. The period of self-examination had been too long, his nature too prudent. . . .

For the true ascetic, and this More was, it was sacrifice to leave the tranquillity of the cloister, to reject the mysteries of contemplative life. The question persists. Why did he so suddenly and so ardently become the busy lawyer, the fervent husband? . . . More's friend Erasmus was of the opinion that it was the question of celibacy which turned More from the spiritual life. "When of a sentimental age, he was not a stranger to the emotions of love," he wrote, "but without loss of character, having no inclination to press his advantage, and being more attracted by a mutual liking than by any licentious object . . . he applied his whole mind to religion, having some thought of taking orders, for which he prepared himself by watchings and fastings and prayers and such like exercises; wherein he showed much more wisdom than the generality of people, who rashly engage in so arduous a profession without testing themselves beforehand. And indeed there was no obstacle to his adopting this kind of life, except the fact that he could not shake off his wish to marry. Accordingly he resolved to be a chaste husband rather than a licentious priest."

In some support of Erasmus' statement that More "was not a stranger to the emotions of love" is a poem he wrote in later years, which was dedicated to an Elizabeth, whom apparently he knew when he was sixteen and she younger. In pretty verse he tells her that the years had passed since first they met but the memory of her remained with him.

32

Severed, our different fates we then pursued,
Till this late date my raptures has renewed.
Crimeless, my heart you stole in life's soft prime,
And still possess that heart without a crime.
Pure was the love which in my youth prevailed,
And age would keep it pure, if honour failed.
O may the gods, who, five long lustres passed,
Have brought us to each other well at last,
Grant, that when numbered five long lustres more,
Healthful, I still may hail thee healthful as before!

"A chaste husband rather than a licentious priest." Once having decided to be a husband, More lost no time in finding a bride. A descendant of the union which he was soon to make, Cresacre More, declares that it was More's confessor who urged him to matrimony. He gives an account of a somewhat odd courtship: "Sir Thomas More having determined by the advice and direction of his ghostly father to be a married man, there was at that time a pleasant . . . gentleman of an ancient family in Essex, one Mr. John Colt . . . that invited him to his house, being much delighted in his company, and proffered unto him the choice of any of his daughters, who were young gentlewomen of very good carriage and complexions, and very religiously inclined, whose honest and sweet conversation, whose virtuous education enflamed Sir Thomas not a little; and although his affection most served him to the second, for that he thought her the fairest and best favored; yet when he thought with himself, that this would be a grief and some blemish in the eldest to see her younger sister preferred before her, he, of a kind of compassion settled his fancy upon the eldest, and soon after married her, with all her friends' good liking."

The role of husband fitted Thomas More awkwardly at the beginning. Jane Colt was ten years his junior. The girl bride missed the companionship of her sisters and liked not at all the exchange of rustic peace for London tumult. The shy girl of seventeen must have had many a tremulous moment when asked to play hostess to such close friends of her husband's as the learned doctors, Grocyn and Linacre, and the Dutch scholar, Erasmus. Besides, More was fresh from the sombre company of the Carthusians. From childhood his companions had been older and serious men. It is true there was that other and lighter side to his nature; he was the man of broad humour who later kept a clown in his house, and monkeys in his garden. But the many heavy excursions into philosophy and theology provided little charm for the new bride, and during the first days of their marriage she was bewildered and distressed.

Early during More's marriage Erasmus came from Rotterdam to visit the More household at Bucklersbury in London, and what he saw there provided him with the basis of a tale which he wrote years later. It was the story of a learned man who endeavoured to educate a young wife by "getting her to repeat the substance of the sermons she heard." Copious weepings and expressions of misery being the only result of such heavy instruction, the husband finally appealed to his father-in-law. "Use your rights," he was told, "and give her a good beating." When the husband refused to adopt such drastic measures, the father feigned such a rage and became so disagreeable that the frightened girl was glad to seek solace in the soothing arms of an understanding husband.

Whatever the reason, the adjustment to each other was quickly made, and with compatibility came an idyllic happiness. A child was expected and during the long wait the young wife cheerfully took lessons in music from her husband, and, with affectionate submission, made effort to share his learning and to absorb his teaching.

Success at the bar was matched by domestic tranquillity. The little misunderstandings between the bride and groom, the scholar and the country miss, had vanished after six years of marriage. Jane had now some understanding of her husband's bent and was not afraid of his distinguished friends. . . .

Throughout the long months of one pregnancy after another, he had moulded her young mind to an appreciation of the delights of the

34

intellect. But it was not all sombre study. There was singing and there were games and there was much romping with the children. There was great joy in the More household, and oftentimes he was disturbed because of the long hours which his profession forced him to spend away from his hearth.

He held a particular devotion to his firstborn, Margaret, which was never to waver and which always was to be reciprocated. "Meg" was his pet name for her. Margaret was only five years old and her young brother not yet a year when their mother, the sweet-natured Jane, suddenly died.

Before a month passed More married again. It was a deliberate action. He had four young children, three of whom were girls, in his house. Professional tasks and civic duties occupied most of his hours. No matter how scrupulously and carefully he acted the father, there still remained the necessity of a mother's care. With this thought in mind he chose a widow, seven years older than himself, Mistress Alice Middleton. Of her children by her first husband, one, Alice, was young enough to be brought up with More's children. It was a practical arrangement, this union. His second wife was a good woman and an efficient housekeeper, although she was never to attain a full understanding of the many sides of her husband's character. Years later Father Bouge, More's parish priest, wrote of the suddenness of the second marriage: "I buried his first wife. And within a month after, he came to me on a Sunday, at night, late, and there he brought me a dispensation to be married the next Monday, without any banns asking . . . This Mr. More was my ghostly child: in his confession to be so pure, so clean, with great study, deliberation, and devotion, I never heard many such . . ."

Jane, the mother of his children, was never forgotten by More. Nearly twenty years later, when he made ready for his own burial, he had her coffin transferred to the grave he thought he would occupy. He wrote his epitaph and in his graceful Latin she took her place as "dear Jane, Thomas More's little wife."

—From *The Story of Thomas More.*

35

I LIKE

THEM

FLUFFY

A. P. HERBERT

Some like them gentle and sweet,
   Some like them haughty and proud,
Some of us like them petite,
   And some of us love the whole crowd;
Some will insist upon grace,
   And some make a point of the pelf,
But, to take a particular case,
   I do like them fluffy myself:

I like them fluffy, I freely confess,
With fluffy blue eyes and a fluffy blue dress,
   With fair fluffy hair, like Love-in-a-mist,
   And lips that declare "I want to be kissed";
      With fluffy soft cheeks, like plums on a wall,
      With a fluffy soft heart—and no brains at all.

36

Some like a girl that's well read,
    Some like a shingle or crop,
But I don't care what's in her head,
    If there's plenty of hair on the top.
Give me the frivolous locks,
    Give me the Gaiety Queen,
Give me the Chocolate Box,
    And give me the Girls' Magazine!

I like them fluffy—I know it's bad taste—
With fluffy soft looks and a flower at the waist,
    With golden hair flying, like mist round the moon,
    And lips that seem sighing, "You must kiss me soon,"
        Not huffy, or stuffy, not tiny or tall,
        But fluffy, just fluffy, with no brains at all.

Brains are all right in their place,
    But oh, it's a shock to the heart
If the lady postpones an embrace
    To enquire your opinions on Art!
And to-day, as I paused on the brink,
    I own I was slightly annoyed
When she sighed and said, "What do you think
    Of the basic assumptions of FREUD?"

"I like them fluffy," I gently replied,
"Not huffy, or stuffy, or puffy with pride,
    With downy soft eyebrows and artful blue eyes,
    The kind that the highbrows pretend to despise,
        With fluffy complexions, like plums on a wall,
        And fluffy opinions, and no brains at all."

        —From *A Book of Ballads.*

TWO WAYS OF LOVE

PAUL CLAUDEL

Dona Prouheze has been placed by her absent husband under the guardianship of Don Balthazar.

DONA PROUHEZE. Yes, Musica, I know the man your heart is waiting for; I am sure he cannot play you false.

DONA MUSICA. Isn't your heart still waiting for someone? But who would dare to threaten your peace when it is under the guardianship of such beauty?

Ah, you were made to run in harness, you and that dreadful man who just now tried to catch me and whose business it is to deal out death.

DONA PROUHEZE. Still you see that Señor Balthazar does not rely on my beauty alone for my defence, but has multiplied the guards around this old castle; I myself asked him to.

DONA MUSICA. Are you so much in love with your prison that you thus take delight in making it more secure?

DONA PROUHEZE. Its bars have to be very strong.

DONA MUSICA. What can the world do against you?

DONA PROUHEZE. No doubt 'tis I that can do much against it.

DONA MUSICA. I don't want any prison.

DONA PROUHEZE. Somebody says that for him prison is where I am not.

DONA MUSICA. I have a prison, and no one can get me out of it.

DONA PROUHEZE. What, Musica?

DONA MUSICA. The arms of the man I love; she is caught, wild Musica!

DONA PROUHEZE. She has escaped! She is only there a moment: who could keep her for ever with a heart like hers?

DONA MUSICA. Already I am with him and he knows it not. It is for my sake, before he knows me,

That, leading his men, he endures as much; it is for me that he feeds the poor and forgives his enemies.

Ah, 'twill not take long to understand that I am joy and that 'tis joy alone, and not the acceptance of sadness, that brings peace.

Yes, I want to mix in every feeling of his like some pleasant sparkling salt to transform and re-pure them. I want to know how he will henceforward set about being sad and doing evil—even when he wants.

I want to be both rare and common to him, like water, like sunshine; water to the thirsting mouth—never the same, when you come to think of it. I want to fill him suddenly and leave him in an instant, and I want him then to have no way of getting me back, neither eyes nor hands, but only the core and that ear within us opening,

Rare and common to him like the rose we inhale from day to day while summer lasts, and yet once only!

That heart that has been waiting for me, ah, what joy for me to fill it!

And if sometimes of a morning the note of a single bird is enough to quench in us the burning of revenge or of jealousy,

What will my soul be to the soul within him, made one with those ineffable chords, in a concert that no one but he has drunk in? His very silence will make me sing!

Where he is I am always with him. And while he works I am the babble of the enamoured fountain!

I am the drowsy turmoil of the great harbour under the noonday sun;

I am the thousand villages on all sides, with the harvests that have no more to fear from the robber or the tax-gatherer;

I, little I, yes, I, am that silly joy on his ugly countenance,

The justice in his heart, that rapture on his face.

DONA PROUHEZE. There is nothing man is less fit for than happiness, nothing he sickens of so soon.

DONA MUSICA. Is he made for suffering?

DONA PROUHEZE. If he asks for it, why refuse him?

DONA MUSICA. How suffer when you are there? Whoever looks at you forgets to live or die.

DONA PROUHEZE. He is not there.

DONA MUSICA. Then there is someone, dearest sister, whose absence is your perpetual company.

DONA PROUHEZE. Little sister, you are over-bold; be quiet! Who would dare to lift his eyes to Prouheze?

DONA MUSICA. Who could tear them away again?

DONA PROUHEZE. Who would trouble her heart?

DONA MUSICA. One voice only in the world, a single voice speaking soft and low.

DONA PROUHEZE, *as if speaking to herself*. . . . inward to this indissoluble sacrament.

DONA MUSICA. Would you have it silent?

DONA PROUHEZE. Ah, by that alone I live!

DONA MUSICA. Do you love him so?

DONA PROUHEZE. How dare you say it? No, I do not love him at all.

DONA MUSICA. Do you regret the time when you did not know him?

DONA PROUHEZE. Now I live for him.

DONA MUSICA. How, when your face is for ever forbidden him?

DONA PROUHEZE. My suffering is not.

DONA MUSICA. Don't you want his happiness?

DONA PROUHEZE. I want him to suffer, too.

DONA MUSICA. He does suffer now.

DONA PROUHEZE. Never enough.

DONA MUSICA. He is calling; will you not answer?

DONA PROUHEZE. To him I am not a voice.

DONA MUSICA. What are you, then?

DONA PROUHEZE. A sword, right through his heart.

—From *The Satin Slipper*.

THREE
WAYS
OF
LOVE

*JOE ROY MEEKS**

Cyrano

ALBERT F. GRIFFITH

Why, of course, I think you're pretty.
That is, I mean I guess you are.
I mean I like your looks I guess.
    You're sort of, you know, peaked—
    Sort of white and soft, that is.
I mean your eyes are pretty, too,
Sort of . . . like a fish: you know
That glimmers underwater
Blue and wet and, you know, glowy.

Oh, I can't say it: what
You know I want to, mean to;
It's just you're sort of,
Well, I guess you're sort of, part of,
You know, all that's everything.

I mean I guess you are.

  * "Joe Roy Meeks," "Mr. Douglas B. Watson" (p. 347) and "Daniel Booter"
(p. 410) are from "Three People Talking" in *Beginnings* by New Catholic Authors.

NORA CRIONA

JAMES STEPHENS

I have looked him round and looked him through,
Know everything that he would do
In such a case, in such a case,
And when a frown comes on his face
I dream of it, and when a smile
I trace its sources in a while.
He cannot do a thing but I
Peep to find the reason why
For I love him, and I seek,
Every evening in the week,
To peep behind his frowning eye
With little query, little pry,
And make him if a woman can
Happier than any man.

Yesterday he gripped her tight
And cut her throat—and serve her right!

42

MARRIAGE IN CHINA

JOHN WU

My wife and I had never seen each other before our wedding, which occurred on April 12, 1916. Both of us were pagans and brought up in the old Chinese way. It was our parents who engaged us to each other, when we were barely six years of age. In my early 'teens, I came to know where her house was. I had an intense desire to have a glimpse of her. In coming back from school, I sometimes took a round-about way so as to pass by the door of her house at the foot of the T'ai Ho Ch'iao, or the "Bridge of Celestial Harmony," in the hope that she might be leaning at the door. But I never had the good fortune to see her.

I have compared notes with my wife and have concluded that our engagement happened this way. When I was six, I was brought by my father to his bank to spend a day there. The manager of the bank next to my father's sent a boy to fetch me to his bank, and he feted me with fruits and everything. I took supper with him, and all the time he was silently beaming at me. I certainly had lived a day as a prince. At night I returned home in my father's sedan-chair.

I did not know why that friend of my father had treated me with such kindness and had smiled at me with such sweetness. It was only later that I came to know that he had chosen me to be the husband of his second daughter! My wife recollects that on the very day when he had seen me, he returned home in the highest spirits, telling her mother, "I have found a husband for Ah-Yu." He even teased his six-year-old daughter by saying, "Ah-Yu, I have got a boy for you. He is handsome and clever!" My wife did not have any reaction at all, for she did not know what "husband" was, thinking that it was humbug.

Nor did I know what "wife" was. I only knew that whatever my father did for me could not but be good. Later I came to realize that I was betrothed to the daughter of that sweet elderly man who had

43

treated me like a prince. I met him many times, and I called him "father-in-law." A genuine affection developed between us. I had such love for him that later, whenever I was angry with my wife, I needed only to remind myself that she was the daughter of her father in order to turn my anger into something like tenderness.

Although I was engaged not by my own will, I had absolutely no doubt that the one to whom my parents had matched me was predestined to be my wife. In one sense, such a betrothal had a greater dignity than the civil engagement by the free choice of the parties; because it was, as it were, registered in Heaven. If one has chosen one's own fiancée, one is liable to wonder at times if one has made the right choice. If, on the other hand, one believes, as we did, that every marriage is made in Heaven, there could be no room for regret, any more than Adam could have regretted that only Eve and none other was given to him.

You can easily imagine then how eagerly I was looking forward to meeting my predestined wife. At long, long last, the day of the wedding arrived. My wife arrived in the flowery-chair. As soon as she got out of the chair, we had to undergo all the complicated marital rites of the old days, including among other ceremonies the *kowtowing* to the tablet on which were written the five characters: Heaven, Earth, Nation, Parents, Teachers. During the ceremony, as we were standing side by side, I tried to look at her through the corner of my eyes, but I did not see her face, because it was heavily veiled. I remember that some of the guests, espying my furtive looks at her, put their fingers on their cheeks, signifying that I was a cheeky bridegroom.

When the ceremony of *kowtowing* was over, we were led into the bridal chamber, where we were placed in front of our bed and made to drink to each other the "love-wine" out of twin cups carved from the same piece of wood. It was only then that I looked my wife in the face, and I loved her at the first sight. She did not see me even then, for she was too bashful to lift her eyes.

After the drinking of the love-wine, we were again led out into the hall to perform many other ceremonies, such as bowing to the elder

44

relatives and friends, and receiving the homage of our nephews and nieces. At the banquet, which was offered in the evening, we served the wine to all the guests. It was not until midnight that we were again led into the bridal chamber and left alone. At last, the door was closed and the guests were shut out, although the more curious ones still tarried in the antechamber to listen to our conversation. May God forgive their itching ears!

As soon as I found myself alone with my wife, a fit of bashfulness overcame both of us. We remained silent for some moments, which

seemed very long. She was too shy and too good to open her mouth first, because she knew that for a wife to speak first would be an omen that the husband would be henpecked. On my part, I was fumbling in my mind for some appropriate subject-matter of conversation. Suddenly I remembered her father, who had been so kind to me when he was living. So I started the conversation stutteringly, thus: "It is too bad, isn't it, that Father-in-law has died? Otherwise how happy he would feel today!"

She looked at me ominously, and answered, "Oh yes, Father was so fond of you."

Another embarrassing silence ensued. I made an attempt to resume the conversation by remarking, "It is too bad, isn't it, that my father should have died so early?"

She looked at me with visible sadness on her face, but remained silent. I thought she was not too easy to talk to. After some moments, I said, "It is too bad, isn't it, that my mother should have died two years ago, when we were scheduled to be wed?"

This time she did not even look at me. I thought it was about time to change the subject, so I asked, "Do you know how to read and write?"

"No," she answered. "Just as I was starting to go to school, your mother sent word to my mother that she would not like to see her future daughter-in-law educated in the modern way."

"Ugh, ugh, that I did not know," was my curt comment.

But I wondered why the bride was so sulky. Did I offend her by mentioning our dear parents? How could that be? The truth is that her mother had taught her that in her first conversation with me there should be no mention of death or anything of that sort, as that would augur ill. I did not know that kind of superstition, as I had no mother to teach me. As it happened, I mentioned death three times in "opening my golden mouth," as a bridegroom's first words to his bride were popularly called in those days. It was only later that my wife confessed to me what she thought of me at the first conversation. She took me for a lunatic, and I don't blame her for that. . . .

To the Western reader, the old Chinese marriage system must appear inconceivable. I remember that when I told my dear friend Dom Edouard Neut, the Belgian Benedictine, about it, he simply could not believe it. All amazed and amused, he asked me, "Do you mean to say that you actually had not seen your wife before you were married?! How could that be?" On my part, I was amazed by his amazement and amused by his amusement. I said to him, "Father, did you choose your parents, your brothers and your sisters? And yet you love them all the same."

God has given a good wife to me, just as He has given me good parents, a good brother and sister, a good body and a good mind, good children, and a good country. I am not trying to justify the old system of marriage, but to make you understand the psychology that made it possible. The same thing is true with the education of women. In the old days, there were no schools for women. The few women writers we have had in history were educated at home, and they were the exceptions. In my childhood days, a girl from a respectable family seen walking on the streets would be talked about in the whole city of Ningpo. So it was quite natural that my wife did not learn to read. But she was *educated* in the family tradition, though not through the reading of books. She was taught by her mother how to behave like a woman, how to perform the domestic duties, etc., with the result that she is full of common sense, which after all is so uncommon. As to her religious faith, she was brought up in exactly the same kind of spiritual atmosphere as I was: the anonymous indigenous religion of the Chinese people, the religion of Heaven and good conscience, the faith that God sees everything, that He prospers the good and punishes the wicked, that all the minor deities are His emissaries, that all religions have but one purpose—to make men good, that to help others is in the long run to help yourself and your children, for God is just and merciful. This is the fundamental faith of the Chinese people. It is the ocean in which they swim freely.

—From *Beyond East and West.*

PERHAPS
HE DIDN'T
LOVE HER

J. B. MORTON

My lover lives in San-Tehung-Pou.
I live in Pe-Si-Hou.
You can easily see one place from the other,
So why on earth isn't he always looking at me?

—From *The Misadventures of Dr. Strabismus.*

THE OLD
FELLOW
OF LYME

There was an old fellow of Lyme,
Who married three wives at a time.
When they asked why the third,
He replied "One's absurd,
And bigamy, Sir, is a crime."

THE EMANCIPATION OF DOMESTICITY

G. K. CHESTERTON

This force upon a man to develop one feature has nothing to do with what is commonly called our competitive system, but would equally exist under any rationally conceivable kind of Collectivism. Unless the Socialists are frankly ready for a fall in the standard of violins, telescopes and electric lights, they must somehow create a moral demand on the individual that he shall keep up his present concentration on these things. It was only by men being in some degree specialist that there ever were any telescopes; they must certainly be in some degree specialist in order to keep them going. It is not by making a man a

State wage-earner that you can prevent him thinking principally about the very difficult way he earns his wages. There is only one way to preserve in the world that high levity and that more leisurely outlook which fulfils the old vision of universalism. That is, to permit the existence of a partly protected half of humanity; a half which the harassing industrial demand troubles indeed, but only troubles indirectly. In other words, there must be in every centre of humanity one human being upon a larger plan; one who does not "give her best," but gives her all.

Our old analogy of the fire remains the most workable one. The fire need not blaze like electricity nor boil like boiling water; its point is that it blazes more than water and warms more than light. The wife is like the fire, or to put things in their proper proportion, the fire is like the wife. Like the fire, the woman is expected to cook: not to excel in cooking, but to cook; to cook better than her husband who is earning the coke by lecturing on botany or breaking stones. Like the fire, the woman is expected to tell tales to the children, not original and artistic tales, but tales—better tales than would probably be told by a first-class cook. Like the fire, the woman is expected to illuminate and ventilate, not by the most startling revelations or the wildest winds of thought, but better than a man can do it after breaking stones or lecturing. But she cannot be expected to endure anything like this universal duty if she is also to endure the direct cruelty of competitive or bureaucratic toil. Woman must be a cook, but not a competitive cook; a school-mistress, but not a competitive school-mistress; a house-decorator, but not a competitive house-decorator; a dressmaker, but not a competitive dressmaker. She should have not one trade but twenty hobbies; she, unlike the man, may develop all her second bests. This is what has been really aimed at from the first in what is called the seclusion, or even the oppression, of women. Women were not kept at home in order to keep them narrow; on the contrary, they were kept at home in order to keep them broad. The world outside the home was one mass of narrowness, a maze of cramped paths, a madhouse of monomaniacs. It was only by partly limiting and protecting the woman that she was enabled to play at five or six professions and so come

50

almost as near to God as the child when he plays at a hundred trades. But the woman's professions, unlike the child's, were all truly and almost terribly fruitful; so tragically real that nothing but her universality and balance prevented them being merely morbid.

This is the substance of the contention I offer about the historic female position. I do not deny that women have been wronged and even tortured; but I doubt if they were ever tortured so much as they are tortured now by the absurd modern attempt to make them domestic empresses and competitive clerks at the same time. I do not deny that even under the old tradition women had a harder time than men; that is why we take off our hats. I do not deny that all these various female functions were exasperating; but I say that there was some aim and meaning in keeping them various. . . .

The shortest way of summarising the position is to say that woman stands for the idea of Sanity; that intellectual home to which the mind must return after every excursion on extravagance. The mind that finds its way to wild places is the poet's; but the mind that never finds its way back is the lunatic's. There must in every machine be a part that moves and a part that stands still; there must be in everything that changes a part that is unchangeable. And many of the phenomena which moderns hastily condemn are really parts of this position of the woman as the centre and pillar of health. Much of what is called her subservience, and even her pliability, is merely the subservience and pliability of a universal remedy; she varies as medicines vary, with the disease. She has to be an optimist to the morbid husband, a salutary pessimist to the happy-go-lucky husband. She has to prevent the Quixote from being put upon, and the bully from putting upon others. The French King wrote—

> "Toujours femme varie
> Bien fol qui s'y fie,"

but the truth is that woman always varies, and that is exactly why we always trust her. . . .

Babies need not to be taught a trade, but to be introduced to a world. To put the matter shortly, woman is generally shut up in a house with a human being at the time when he asks all the questions that there are, and some that there aren't. It would be odd if she retained any of the narrowness of a specialist. Now if anyone says that this duty of general enlightenment (even when freed from modern rules and hours, and exercised more spontaneously by a more protected person) is in itself too exacting and oppressive, I can understand the view. I can only answer that our race has thought it worth while to cast this burden on women in order to keep common sense in the world. But when people begin to talk about this domestic duty as not merely difficult but trivial and dreary, I simply give up the question. For I cannot with the utmost energy of imagination conceive what they mean. When domesticity, for instance, is called drudgery, all the difficulty arises from a double meaning in the word. If drudgery only means dreadfully hard work, I admit the woman drudges in the home, as a man might drudge at the Cathedral of Amiens or drudge behind a gun at Trafalgar. But if it means that the hard work is more heavy because it is trifling, colourless and of small import to the soul, then, as I say, I give it up; I do not know what the words mean. To be Queen Elizabeth within a definite area, deciding sales, banquets, labours and holidays; to be Whiteley within a certain area, providing toys, boots, sheets, cakes and books; to be Aristotle within a certain area, teaching morals, manners, theology, and hygiene; I can understand how this might exhaust the mind, but I cannot imagine how it could narrow it. How can it be a large career to tell other people's children about the Rule of Three, and a small career to tell one's own children about the universe? How can it be broad to be the same thing to everyone, and narrow to be everything to someone? No; a woman's function is laborious, but because it is gigantic, not because it is minute. I will pity Mrs. Jones for the hugeness of her task; I will never pity her for its smallness.

—From *What's Wrong with the World.*

DEPARTURE

COVENTRY
PATMORE It was not like your great and gracious ways!
Do you, that have nought other to lament,
Never, my Love, repent
Of how, that July afternoon,
You went,
With sudden, unintelligible phrase,
And frighten'd eye,
Upon your journey of so many days,
Without a single kiss, or a good-bye?
I knew, indeed, that you were parting soon;
And so we sate, within the low sun's rays,
You whispering to me, for your voice was weak,
Your harrowing praise.
Well, it was well
To hear you such things speak,
And I could tell
What made your eyes a growing gloom of love,
As a warm South-wind sombres a March grove.
And it was like your great and gracious ways
To turn your talk on daily things, my Dear,
Lifting the luminous, pathetic lash
To let the laughter flash,
Whilst I drew near,
Because you spoke so low that I could scarcely hear.
But all at once to leave me at the last,
More at the wonder than the loss aghast,
With huddled, unintelligible phrase,
And frighten'd eye,
And go your journey of all days
With not one kiss, or a good-bye,
And the only loveless look the look with which you pass'd:
'Twas all unlike your great and gracious ways.

SO GENIUS NEEDS A MUSE?

ETIENNE GILSON

I. PETRARCH AND LAURA

Francesco Petrarch saw Laura for the first time on the 6th of April, 1327, at the hour of Prime in the Church of St. Clare at Avignon, whither both had gone for their Holy Week devotions. Francesco was then in his twenty-third year. This worldly, elegant young clerk who never had received and never would receive even a minor ecclesiastical order, merely sought from the Church a career in which he could freely follow his passionate love of literature. We know nothing with certainty about the identity of her whom he called Laura. . . . Was she still a girl or already married when Petrarch first looked upon her? There are arguments on both sides. The one thing certain is that she existed, that Petrarch saw her, and that this meeting of the 6th of April, 1327, left in his heart a thorn from which he suffered long. . . .

Laura's own feelings were doubtless badly mixed. Pleasure at being the theme of her poet's song, admiration, friendship and perhaps more than friendship, were all seeking justification in the mission of his moral redemption which she certainly believed to be hers. Laura wanted to cure Petrarch of the wound she had involuntarily inflicted—but this does not wholly explain why she kept him in play so long with smiles and discreet encouragement, changing into the severity she deemed necessary every time the imprudently encouraged poet attempted to advance a step further. Of all the Muses we know, Laura will always be the model. For the very art of being a Muse is to nourish love in the poet, to let him realize that she loves him—that in fact she loves him much too well ever to grant him anything. . . .

The amazing vitality of the poet's love for his Muse is due to the fact that from its very birth it was set free from Time. Petrarch was, of course, unwaveringly faithful to his love, but the only Laura he loved

55

was the girl he saw first in her youth, whom he loved still in the woman worn out by age and sickness who outlived her. Re-read only that sad sonnet, No. LXI, written when Laura's beauty was beginning to fade. Where are the golden locks scattered by the wind and the eyes full of a fire "that today is so lacking"? All that is in the past, but the lovely glow of the first vision is still intact, and after so many years the poet's love still lives upon it: "A heavenly spirit, a living sun I saw, and even though today all that is changed, a slackened bow does not cure the wound it inflicted."

Is Petrarch here showing a characteristic irony? Nothing of the kind. It is rather the exquisite accuracy of his words we must admire, for their precision is too cruel not to have been calculated. The urge felt by certain great poets to keep faith will never be better expressed. Laura as he will see her henceforward would be quite unable to pierce him with a new wound, yet she alone can bring back the pain of the first, which she alone inflicted. It matters little, then, if Laura changes as she lives on. The fidelity sworn by the poet is out of reach of Time, and its destructiveness for its object is enthroned in a past that he cannot touch. When Laura died Petrarch lost the woman who alone could bring back to him her whom he had loved since the 6th of April, 1327; and whom since that day Laura had merely outlived. Yet she could never die so long as Petrarch lived. . . .

Laura had made a great poet out of a little clerk absorbed in his Latin. Petrarch at least is convinced of this, and as he never asks whether his own genius may, after all, have created Laura, it would be very ungracious of us to ask it in his name. "If beautiful things have come forth from me," he says elsewhere, "the seeds were sown by you."

II. BAUDELAIRE AND APOLLONIE

Baudelaire knew that Madame Sabatier might cause him some anxiety. He took pains to keep her in her part in the act: the part of goddess—a role to which she was not at all suited. On the 18th of

August, 1857, five years after his first anonymous letter, he wrote, "When I do something good I tell myself: here is something to bring me nearer to her *in spirit*." The italics in the quotations are always his, and no man has ever told a woman more clearly and more persistently, "I do not desire you." It is not surprising, then, that when the goddess came down of her own accord from the pedestal, which she had found extremely boring, her worshipper could not meet her desires by managing to treat her as an ordinary woman. The experts, of whom I am not one, disagree about what happened, the best-informed actually state that nothing happened at all. This is a possibility, although the famous letter of the 31st of August, 1857, could be interpreted in two ways. Anyhow, if nothing did happen that day, it was certainly because Baudelaire, far from ever desiring that anything should happen, had taken infinite precautions to prevent it. . . .

This lover certainly lacks enthusiasm, but it is the poet within him who is on the watch. The great and determining objection is stated none the less clearly from being stated last: "And then, and then, a few days ago you were a goddess, helpful, beautiful, unattainable. Now you are only a woman."

How serenely cruel he is, how pitiless. Baudelaire does not yet know whether he has gained a mistress or for how long, but he knows very well that he has lost his Muse. His Inspiration is dead. She was his idol, but a profaned divinity is no longer sacred. She was his religion, but how can he go on believing when the unattainable ideal of which she was the symbol has turned into a reality of the most commonplace kind? "Never meet or never part" is the fine motto with which Madame Sabatier sealed her last letter. But did she really understand its solemnity? The "never meet" expresses the treason of his Inspiration, for "this positively means that it would have been much better never to have known one another, but that once together we should never part. Such a motto would be very funny on a letter of farewell."

This is really rather horrible, for the letter he is writing is actually the poet's farewell to the Muse he has just lost. Since we have come to know one another let us try never to part, but all the same it remains positively true "that it would be far better had we never met." However, the mischief is done. "Let what may happen, happen. I am a bit of a fatalist. But what I do know is that I have a horror of passion because I know it in all its falseness and the deeply loved image which has ruled over all my life's events is becoming too seductive." And one last touch towards the end of the letter, "Goodbye, my dear, dear beloved. I have rather a grudge against you for being too charming." . . .

She had not really the physique for the job of Baudelaire's mistress, but she did have for the job of his Muse—for that all she lacked was the soul. And so, offering the man the thing he did not want, she deprived the poet of the one thing he did.

It must be said in all fairness to her that she saw quite clearly what she should have been in order that her offer might be acceptable: you have only to read the unhappy letter she promptly posted to her poet: "Look, dear, shall I tell you my thought, a bitter thought and one that hurts me a lot? I think you do not love me." Nothing could have been more true, in the only meaning of the word love that she could understand. "You have no faith in me," she goes on, "but then you have no love. What answer can you give: is it not perfectly clear?" Alas, it was indeed. To the poet's appeal for the eternal feminine, the well-meaning woman replied by offering him Apollonie Sabatier.

III. WAGNER AND MATHILDE

In 1851 Wagner made the acquaintance of Otto Wesendonk, a rich businessman, devoted to the arts, and of his wife Mathilde, aged twenty, very friendly and a good musician. Obviously, what with the wife's charms and the husband's money, it was the ideal household. Art, of course, was all he had in mind: we must not imagine Wagner cold-bloodedly working out all the ways in which such a situation could be turned to his advantage, or even to the advantage of his music. Not calculation so much as a sort of animal instinct was continually bringing him into situations which he was amazed to find so helpful to his art! And if he did not plan the detail of events in advance, when they happened he knew well enough that he had expected them, wanted them, and, to an extent anyhow, helped to produce them.

The drawback to all these love affairs was certainly that Isolde generally belonged to some King Mark or other. . . .

To what an extent *Tristan* alone dominates the entire story can be seen in the homage Wagner pays to Mathilde on Saint Sylvester's day, 1857, when sending her the rough draft of his first act:

> All is blissful
> Beyond pain's reach,
> Free and pure,
> Thine to eternity—
> The anguish
> And the renunciation
> Of Tristan and Isolde.
> Their tears, their kisses,
> In music's sheer gold
> I lay at thy feet,
> That they may give praise to the angel
> Who has raised me so high.

In this total triumph of art, real life was so brutally ignored—for *Tristan* as he came to birth stifled in his embrace everything he could lay hold of—that its reaction was bound to be vigorous. Accustomed though she was to her fantastic husband's ways, Minna realized that this time there was real danger of losing him. Otto Wesendonk, even with the lava of this volcanic genius flooding over him, did not push his love of music to the point where he was willing to sacrifice his wife, the mother of his children, and his home itself. Wagner and Mathilde had to come to a decision—either do what Liszt and Marie d'Agoult had done or else separate.

They separated, and it would be highly interesting to fathom the meaning of a sacrifice the motives for which they had difficulty in explaining to themselves. . . .

The artist had henceforward one mission: so to live with his art as to console Mathilde by giving her back their love eternally transfigured in the perfection of a masterpiece. At Venice he completed *Tristan,* pure essence of Mathilde and yet his own work—so fully that to keep Mathilde for himself and to keep himself for his work have become one and the same thing: "To keep you for me is to keep myself for my work.". . .

"I do not think I saw you clearly [Wagner writes after they met once more], thick mists separated us through which we scarcely heard the sound of each other's voice. You also, I fancy, did not see me, a ghost entered your house in my place. Did you recognize me?" . . .

I hope it will not seem too startling if I say, with full awareness of the difference in the events, the inflections and the very different levels, that this return of 1859, while not at all its equivalent, is comparable with the morrow of the Baudelaire-Sabatier love affair. In both cases the poet was confronted with the woman, and in neither case did he recognize her. It was not when he was gazing upon Madame Wesendonk that Wagner saw the true Mathilde but when he was gazing at Isolde. Nor is it where Wagner is present that Madame Wesendonk recognizes him, it is where Tristan is that she sees Wagner. . . .

For Wagner, for Mathilde, so well aware of the greatness of the work with which the imperious genius of the poet had associated her, everything went on as though they belonged no longer to this world but to another, better, purer, wholly justified by its very perfection, to which they could only gain access by renouncing this one. This language reminds us irresistibly of another to which the masters of a spirituality not only purer but of a different order have long familiarized us. And it comes back to us later when we read again the strange phrase in which this man, devoured by human passions, declared to Mathilde Wesendonk that he sometimes felt himself on the verge of sanctity. . . .

60

IV. COMTE AND CLOTILDE

According to rule, Comte's passionate love broke out at the exact moment when it was needed for his work. "The deciding attack of this virtuous passion coincided last year with the initial working out of my second great work." . . . Comte was suffering from the great anguish of a genius in childbirth, and was ready for that midwifery in reverse where the woman delivers the man from the burden he is carrying, so that overwhelmed with gratitude he often imagines that it was she who had conceived it. . . .

The husband of Madame Clotilde de Vaux, a teacher at Meru, had run away in 1839 leaving an empty cash box behind him. He was never seen again. After less than four years of marriage this delightful young woman of twenty-four found herself alone, entirely destitute, not even a widow, but in the eyes of the law the legitimate wife of a swindler on the run. . . . Comte felt about his wife what Clotilde felt about her husband, and he too had to bear the slavery of a separation that yet held him with an unbreakable chain. She was still the wife of Monsieur de Vaux. He was still the husband of Caroline Massin. Like her he was without home or children, like her he was exiled from family joys. In short, when he compared the position of Clotilde de Vaux with his own he saw in her the vict'm, "more unhappy than he and more spotless, of a similar calamity, so that her moral liberty of action was even more strongly founded than his." Overwhelmed by exactly similar misfortune, were they not morally free to unite their tragedies and to console one another?

Of all the stories of this type there is none better known to us, and the hundred and eighty-three letters which make up their correspondence would really be an *embarras de richesses* were it not that everything worked out in closest conformity with the traditional pattern. Comte's first letter, for naturally he is the first one to write, is dated April the 30th, 1845, at midday. He offers Clotilde a translation of Fielding's *Tom Jones* of which he himself possesses the original. The

usual thanks follow and the usual courtesies, a visit from Clotilde to
Comte, visits from Comte to Clotilde at the home of her parents.
Nothing could be more normal. Clotilde, as we have said, was extremely
intelligent, lonely, unhappy and even despairing. It can be imagined
that the society of such a man as Comte was a very pleasant distraction
for her, all the more because his age, his appearance, his rank as a
master of ideas and his solemn language in no way announced a probable lover. It is clear that she did not understand him, but his lettter
of the 17th of May, 1845, should have been warning enough, for the
philosopher was already speaking of the "sweet unity of feeling" which
had gradually drawn him towards her. She had made a mistake, and
her mistake helps us to understand the psychology of certain Muses.
Clotilde would never have the slightest physical love for Comte, but
she did love him all the same, sincerely and perhaps deeply. The
brotherhood of mind and heart which he had offered at first, and with
which he had to be satisfied at last, was for her a precious and unhoped-
for boon, the only comfort she could still receive from man, this woman
who hoped for none from the God in whom she did not believe. Their
wholly spiritual intercourse could be something very beautiful, and in
one sense it was: but the young woman soon saw simply one more
misfortune added to all that already overwhelmed her when Comte,
having awakened in her heart the mirage of this oasis, startlingly un-
leashed a wild beast which began to lay it waste.

That the philosopher should promise to dedicate to her his *Système
de politique positive* was pleasing enough. When he declared that "by
restoring to life the play of his sweetest private feelings" she would
effectually assist his philosophic impetus, this too was quite acceptable.
It all meant the offer of a role as Muse of Positivism which nothing
forbade her to play. But when Comte talked of "these precious feelings,
these intimate outpourings, these delicious tears" which brought him
"enrapturing vigils" and even made him ill, Clotilde understood very
well what he was really telling her. . . .

Clotilde is in the great tradition of letter-writing women who know
that everything can be said if you never raise your voice. But she was

miles away from suspecting what was really happening. . . .

In an immense letter of August the 5th, 1845, the philosopher explains to Clotilde that, thanks to her, his personal affections will tend directly to the perfecting of his social action. Like Wagner, he found himself by a miracle in the situation called for to complete his work. He ended an interminable discourse by saying to his Muse, "I trust that after these explanations you can be in no real doubt about the happy philosophic results which I expect from our eternal friendship." She has already become "St. Clotilde," and it is in a pious attitude of mind that he undertakes his second great work. His more practical Muse borrows fifty francs from him on the 11th of August, 1845. Comte is enchanted, offers her more and, far from being discouraged, raises an "altar" to Clotilde in front of which he invokes her as a refreshment from his work and feels the birth of his highest inspirations.

The "cult" of Clotilde was born; not just a simple sentimental veneration, but a concrete worship of which Comte was to remain the priest up to the end of his life. . . .

There were, of course, minor crises, for every time Clotilde offered him her "heart," Comte hoped anew for the rest of her. . . . Clotilde wrote him that she had taken a purgative; he replied that every morning in front of her altar he recited his loving prayer to Saint Clotilde and re-read extracts from her letters, "those most suitable to mark out the steps in their holy love." Nothing discouraged him, nor for that matter her either. Henceforward they were to go forward "leaning upon each other," exchanging from time to time the affectionate kiss of friends, hardly knowing which gave or which received it, in a pitiable confusion of love, jealousy, music, Positivism, money and cod liver oil—until the final catastrophe, when Clotilde, after a last attempt to offer him more than her friendship, died in Comte's arms. They were alone, for he had shut the door of her room in the face of her bewildered parents. . . .

—From *A Choir of Muses.*

BREACH OF PROMISE OF MARRIAGE

W. S. GILBERT

The Defendant Addresses the Jury

O gentlemen, listen, I pray
   Though I own that my heart has been ranging,
Of nature the laws I obey,
   For nature is constantly changing.
The moon in her phases is found,
   The time, and the wind, and the weather,
The months in succession come round,
   And you don't find two Mondays together.
      Consider the moral, I pray,
      Nor bring a young fellow to sorrow,
      Who loves this young lady today,
      And loves that young lady tomorrow!

You cannot eat breakfast all day
   Nor is it the act of a sinner,
When breakfast is taken away,
   To turn your attention to dinner;
And it's not in the range of belief,
   That you could hold him as a glutton,
Who, when he is tired of beef,
   Determines to tackle the mutton.
      But this I am ready to say,
      If it will diminish their sorrow,
      I'll marry this lady today,
      And I'll marry that lady tomorrow!

THE WHALE'S WOOING

G. K. CHESTERTON

A newspaper famous for its urgency about practical and pressing affairs recently filled a large part of its space with the headline, "Do Whales Have Two Wives?" There was a second headline saying that Science was about to investigate the matter in a highly exact and scientific fashion. And indeed it may be hoped that science is more exact than journalism. One peculiarity of that sentence is that it really says almost the opposite of what it is intended to say. We might suppose that, before printing a short phrase in large letters, a man might at least look at it to see whether it said what he meant. But behind all this hustle there is not only carelessness but a great weariness. Strictly speaking, the phrase, "Do Whales Have Two Wives?" could only mean, if it meant anything, "Do all the whales, in their collective capacity, have only two wives between them?" But the journalist did not mean to suggest this extreme practice of polyandry. He only meant to ask whether the individual whale can be reproached with the practice of bigamy. At first sight there is something rather quaint and alluring about the notion of watching a whale to see whether he lives a double life. A whale scarcely seems designed for secrecy or for shy and furtive flirtation. The thought of a whale assuming various disguises, designed to make him inconspicuous among other fishes, puts rather a strain on the imagination. He would have to keep his two establishments, one at the North

65

Pole and the other at the South, if his two wives were likely to be jealous of each other; and if he really wished to avoid becoming a bone (or whale-bone) of contention. In truth the most frivolous philanderer would hardly wish to conduct his frivolities on quite so large a scale; and the loves of the whales may well appear a theme for a bolder pen than any that has yet traced the tremendous epic of the loves of the giants.

But we have a sort of fancy or faint suspicion about where it may end. Science, or what journalism calls Science, is always up to its little games; and this might possibly be one of them. We know how some people perpetually preach to us that there is no morality in nature and therefore nothing natural in morality. We know we have been told to learn everything from the herd instinct or the law of the jungle; to learn our manners from a monkey-house and our morals from a dog-fight. May we not find a model in a far more impressive and serene animal? Shall we not be told that Leviathan refuses to put forth his nose to the hook of monogamy, and laughs at the shaking of the chivalric spear? To the supine and superstitious person, who has lingered with one wife for a whole lifetime, will not the rebuke be uttered in the ancient words: "Go to the whale, thou sluggard"? Contemplating the cetaceous experiments in polygamy, will not the moralist exclaim once more: "How doth the little busy whale improve the shining hour!" Will not the way of this superior mammal be a new argument for the cult of the new Cupid; the sort of Cupid who likes to have two strings to his bow? For we are bound to regard the monster as a moral superior, according to the current moral judgments. We are perpetually told that the human being is small, that even the earth itself is small, compared with the splendid size of the solar system. If we are to surrender to the size of the world, why not to the size of the whale? If we are to bow down before planets which are larger than our own, why not before animals that are larger than ourselves? Why not, with a yet more graceful bow, yield the *pas* (if the phrase be sufficiently aquatic) to the great mountain of blubber? In many ways he looks very like the highest moral ideal of our time.

—From *The Coloured Lands*.

BETTER AVOID TOULON

There was a young girl of Toulong
Who sang a most scandalous song.
It was not her words
That startled the birds
But the terrible double ongtong.

FOURTH DIMENSIONZ

SISTER MARY JEAN DORCY

That z, for instance; I wasn't aiming at z. But that's what this essay is about; gremlins. In this climate, even nice people have them.

A couple of years ago someone did a Ph.D. thesis on pencil sharpeners. We may yet have a brave and venturesome individual who will go out into the no-man's-land of the little people and do us a good research paper about gremlins. If you know anyone who is working on this thankless task, send him to me. I have first-hand information.

67

Gremlins, as is commonly known, got their start in airplane engines during the last war. In their meetings they chatted subversively about ailerons and air pockets. After wreaking havoc all during the war they were demobilized and, quite without being asked, got jobs in civilian life. There is now hardly a desk-drawer in the country that isn't infested, and DDT won't reach them. Fact is, they eat it like peanuts.

The Western, or blue-footed, gremlin is a slightly smaller form of the buffled gremlin of the Eastern seaboard, but lacks the membrane between the seventh and eighth toes. Its song is a squeak like the sound of a distant window sliding up at night, and in nesting season this changes to the sound of a venetian blind flapping next door. It is a shy creature, and nests in inaccessible spots—down bath-tub drains, under low dressers, and out over stairways. Its special work is to snap window shades up where you cannot reach them, and secrete stepladders, hammers, dustmops and door keys where you cannot find them. It also hides the soap in the bath tub.

The pileated gremlin (typus erasus typus erasus) makes cunning little nests in typewriters, using the fine downy eraser dust for lining the nest. Its cry is a low pileat, whatever that is; I suspect that is why it is called a pileated gremlin. This is the creature that keeps putting commas where the "m" was last time you looked, transposes "u" and "i" and sp4lls words with n8mbers. When ha½½y it can really mix things up for you. When well-fed it purrs contentedly and skips around, causing the ty p ewri ter to do the same. Its favorite trick is to get the carbon paper in backwards so that you have to stand on your head to read your manuscript. When the typewriter is in use, this friendly little creature rides the ribbon, looping it around any convenient gadget, and it often crawls into the ribbon reverse for a cosy nap. The ½ileated gremlin is always trying to improve itself and often takes home-study courses in fingerprinting which it practices on your manuscripts. Only in very dry seasons will this harmless little creature drink the ink out of your fountain pen. . . .

There is nothing a gremlin likes better than to get into an orderly desk drawer. Here he hides paper clips, spills rubber bands, punches holes in tubes of glue, and shuffles notes. The only thing you can do is to build a trap. Now, mine is a very simple but effective type of box trap, the design of which I am going to send in to *Good Housekeeping*. It is a small cardboard box which says, innocently enough, "Dennison's Gummed Labels." What could be plainer? Good, says the gremlin; here's an orderly soul—she even *labels* things. (Gremlins talk to themselves.) So he opens it, and what does he find? Dennison's Gummed Labels? The box contains a razor blade, three small buttons and one large one, two rusty paper clips, a suitcase key (I am sure it is a suitcase key; it doesn't fit anything else), a name tape, a short length of fishline, and a very dusty pill that I think is an aspirin. Fancy the shattered nerves with which that gremlin must face life after he pulls himself together. He'll never pry open another box. Not in *my* desk drawer.

A friend of mine has what he claims is a better one. It consists of a metal tube plainly marked "Bouillon Cubes," and contains several small screw-eyes, an Indian-head penny, the working parts of a fountain-pen, and some pins. Another friend—who, it seems to me, rather overdoes things—has a small box labelled "Torrone; La Florentine Brand; almond candy." On one side is a friendly-looking gentleman with Smith Brother whiskers and on the other, a fair maiden—possibly the captain's daughter from the "Hesperus"—is leaping into the sea from a wrecked ship. She (the owner of the trap, that is) claims that the gremlins never get any further than the rather puzzling decorations on the cover, and that they have not yet discovered that the box is full of small buttons. I would be afraid, personally, that the little creatures would get delusions of grandeu4 from having an imported box in their drawer, but I cannot deny that it gives a tone to the place.

The solicitude with which these devoted little creatures give my mail special handling is enough to wring tears out of a stone. I am probably the only person in the country who ever had a package take six weeks from San Francisco to Minneapolis. Some poor little flat-footed gremlin had walked all the way with it. My smallest packages get the undivided attention of the man-who-pounds-corners-off, and they keep a special puddle handy in which to set the larger boxes.

My large portfolios get uniform treatment; after the man gets the corners off, they set a drum of oil on the middle unless there is an elephant free to step on it. Whenever a package comes into the local post office looking like a pancake that has been left out in the rain, with the address obliterated and only a streak of ball-point ink to indicate which is the top, my gremlins go down and bring it to me, and hide the return address to make it all a delightful secret.

Other people can mail packages that tick and rattle and smoke in a sinister fashion, but I can't get the flattest manuscript past the clerk without him demanding to know if it's full of bombs or boll-weevils. Other folk can order art material from Little America and it arrives intact; I can't even get it across the Bay Bridge, and if it gets here in one piece it's the wrong piece. I am still waiting to hear how my order for a Latin dictionary turned out to be a box of small pink shells, but the gremlins probably know all about it. The same gremlin that takes care of these things puts my name on all the "sucker" lists throughout the country, entitling me to life memberships in all the wild schemes of people who use the mail for shenanigans. I get letters from people I never heard of, wanting to sell me things I don't want. Remembering my brother, whose sudden death revealed no less than seven memberships in the "Necktie-of-the-Month Club" (not because he fancied neckties, but because he just couldn't say No to the little boys who sold them), it makes my blood run cold.

There is a solid precedent in religious houses for the slightly fey but harmless occupants of the unseen world best interpreted by the Irish. Look back to the Book of Kells: it swarms with unbelievable little creatures born of a sailor's isolation. For the Kells monks, and those of many of the island monasteries, belonged to the tradition of the sea wanderers who christened Greenland "Irland it Mikla" (Greater Ireland) while the rest of Europe was drawing the world square. How do we know they were seafaring men? It's very simple if you have ever tried to copy one of those waggish capitals from Kells or the Lindisfarne Gospels; the long, carefully-interwoven decorations are not mere embroidery, they are ropes. They have continuity, and you could untangle them if you had patience enough, and good eyesight. Nobody but a sailor could have worked out the intricate knots in the simplest Celtic design. And there is a certain untrammeled imaginative quality about the beasties; they look to be of seafaring ancestry. I know, there is a religious significance to all of the figures, most of which will never be deciphered now. The beast so entangled in ropes and meshes is the devil, caught in the net of his own lies. These are not desert animals, the like of which Anthony and Pachomius might have seen; these are sea animals, with fins and tails, cousins of the Loch Ness monster.

So, my smart little gremlins—where on earth is that eraser?—you see that you are not so original. I am not afraid of you. The Irish monks of more than a thousand years ago were on to all your antics. You couldn't play tricks on their printing the way you do with my typewriter but you just wa8t. Y ou j7t wait. 7ou just 2ait. Oh, we;;.

—From *Shepherd's Tartan.*

71

THE OLD OMAR

OMAR KHAYYÁM

A Book of Verses underneath the Bough,
   A Jug of Wine, a Loaf of Bread—and Thou
Beside me singing in the Wilderness—
   Oh, Wilderness were Paradise enow!

THE NEW OMAR

G. K. CHESTERTON

A book of verses underneath the bough,
   Provided that the verses do not scan:
A flask of wine, a loaf of bread and thou,
   Short-haired, all angles, looking like a man;

But let the wine be unfermented, pale,
   Of chemicals compounded, Lord knows how,
This were indeed the Prophet's Paradise—
   Ah Paradise were wilderness enow.

—From *Collected Poems.*

THE NEWEST OMAR

A jug and a book and a dame,
And a nice shady nook for the same.

ABOUT ROLAND MILK

J. B. MORTON

"The sudden fame that has come to Mr. Clifford King, the Brighton poet, quite frankly disgusts me," said Mr. Roland Milk yesterday.

He came to see me, bringing with him a valise full of verse and a portmanteau stuffed with Press cuttings. These he showed me, grumbling all the time at what he called the crass idiocy of the public. Some of the tributes paid to him are certainly astounding. Here are a few of them, after the publication of his *Oblong Fog, and Other Verses* (Footle and Huff, 5s.).

"Never have I read such . . . poems."—*Times Lit. Supp.*

"Undoubtedly the . . . book of verse published this year."—*The Morgue.*

"One really does not know what to say of this book."—*The Mausoleum.*

"Not since Effie Hagge's *Grumbling Trellis* has there been such a . . ." —*The Freak.*

"Oh!"—*Jam-Fancier's Gazette.*

"It is really time somebody . . . this sort of . . ."—*Chips.*

"Not a . . . moment in the whole book."—*The Criterion.*

"Only a . . . could have written such . . ."—"The Mumbler" in *Poesy.*

BALLADE OF UNSUCCESSFUL MEN

HILAIRE BELLOC

I

The cause of all the poor in '93:
　　The cause of all the world at Waterloo:
The shouts of what was terrible and free
　　Behind the guns of *Vengeance* and her crew:
The Maid that rode so straightly and so true
　　And broke the line to pieces in her pride—
They had to chuck it up; it wouldn't do;
　　The Devil didn't like them, and they died.

II

Cæsar and Alexander shall agree
　　That right athwart the world their bugles blew:
And all the lads that marched in Lombardy
　　Behind the young Napoleon charging through:
All that were easy swordsmen, all that slew
The Monsters, and that served our God and tried
The temper of this world—they lost the clue.
　　The Devil didn't like them, and they died.

III

You, the strong sons of anger and the sea,
　　What darkness on the wings of battle flew?
Then the great dead made answer: "Also we
　　With Nelson found oblivion: Nelson, who
When cheering out of Portsmouth harbour grew
　　To make one purpose with the wind and tide—

74

Our nameless hulks are sunk and rotted through:
The Devil didn't like us and we died."

Envoi

Prince, may I venture (since it's only you)
To speak discreetly of the Crucified?
He was extremely unsuccessful too:
The Devil didn't like Him, and He died.

—From *Sonnets and Verse.*

SATURDAY NIGHT

CARYLL HOUSELANDER

There is something mysterious about Saturday night. It is a night of quickening, of the heightening and raising of psychological temperatures. It is pay day, when, whether one should spend it or not, for a few hours one has money to spend, and for a few hours there is freedom from office, factory and shop. Whatever happens on Saturday night can be slept off on Sunday morning. Tomorrow morning there is no work, there is no alarm clock, no shout of "time to get up."

Tomorrow no one will be a cog in a machine, a voice in a chorus of voices, a face in a multitude of faces, tomorrow everyone will be himself or herself, even if only by dropping out for a few hours.

On Saturday night the streets come alive, the routine is broken, the tension is off, there is the chink of money, the public houses are lit up and noisy. On week days the same public houses are there too, but they are quieter, different, some of them have even a kind of secrecy; they are places where it is sometimes possible to get away, to be warm, to be alone; there are some down the side streets that are furtive. But on Saturday night, they are loud and light and noisy, kindly and quarrelsome. After a few drinks, feeling runs higher, human nature is more vulnerable, more defenceless, sentiment flows over and spills into indiscriminate love-making. A spark of anger blazes up suddenly into a fire that is out of hand.

The darkness on Saturday night has its own quality. It is no longer a cover laid silently over the ardours and sorrows and sweetness of the world. It hums and throbs and sings; it is splashed and fretted with light. The doors of the pubs swing open and shut, gusts of sound and light spatter the pavement, there are sudden glimpses of men and women dark upon a glow of gold, and sudden bursts of laughter or of noisy weeping. Sometimes all the darkness of the night and all its laughter and all its sobbing are gathered and swung between the pavement and the stars in the music of an accordion.

The boys and girls out of the factories walk hand in hand in the streets. They are lovely with the slender loveliness of the poor when they are young. The girls blossom in just the way of those "Japanese Flowers" that children drop into water as a tiny round circle which immediately wriggles and puts out tendrils of yellow, vermilion, emerald and blue, that twist and writhe and sprout into fantastic little flowers. . . .

The very young factory workers walk hand in hand through the gold-fretted darkness, dreaming and shy, shaken with the glory of one another, breathless with the swift new passion of innocence on fire.

There is also intense activity in the Catholic Church. Saturday night is bath night. It is also the bath night of souls. Of course people go to Confession on all the other days and nights too. But Saturday is an accepted night when every Catholic, everywhere in the world, knows that he will find the Church buzzing with a business-like activity that is no outward showing of the unutterable mystery that is taking place, and is often shocking to the uninitiated. No wonder, for even in its holiest acts, human nature is imperfect and there is shoving, pushing, muttering and gate-crashing, even in the queue outside the confessional. Since the Lord commands that the tares and the wheat be left growing together until His coming, you must, until that blessed day, have your viciously pious old lady, who prods her neighbour with her umbrella in Confession queues, side by side with the lowly and humble of heart who is prodded, and the penitent, who unconscious of the mote in his brother's eye, prays undisturbed and unnoticed, his whole being withdrawn into the stillness of love.

When Father O'Grady hurried into church, his penitents were already waiting for him, like a hungry and impatient bread line. He had hardly time to put on his stole before the first two were in, one on each side, like two hungry birds waiting their crumb of heaven.

They were simple people, who understood very little about the grace that they were receiving—some of them, if they *had* understood, would have fought shy of the torrent of light that was being poured over them. Their ears were tuned to the undertones of this world, their eyes used to its grey twilights. They could not have borne the splendour of the God Who came to them in this narrow box, but for the divine ingenuity of His love, which used their very blindness and deafness and denseness for His disguise and came to them clothed in their own limitations.

Father O'Grady understood his people; he knew that they were coming to be fed. Penance is sorrow for sin and forgiveness, but it is much more too. It is the Good Shepherd feeding His sheep, feeding His lambs, and a crumb of the Bread of Life is the whole of life.

He closed his eyes and murmured the first blessing. A scruffy little acolyte told the usual story on one side, a very old woman told it on the other. After them came the long line of pious women hankering after consolation, the emotionally starved hungering for a little sweetness, a little taste of sugar on the living Bread, the young men who found it so difficult to make a firm purpose of amendment and to try to avoid the dangerous occasions of sin, the boys and girls, the devout old men, the aging Children of Mary who were eager to confess their neighbour's sins as well as their own, the sailors who had met temptation under bluer skies and in lovelier guise than it is met in Riverside, the mothers who must hurry so that the fathers who were minding the children could come after them, and the children who had only lately made their First Confessions and still came quite simply to receive the embrace of their little Lord.

As time wore on, a few drifted in from the streets, who, if they were not drunk, had, as the Irish say, "drink taken"; and when they had said, "Bless me, Father, for I have sinned," they were apt to begin to weep. Father O'Grady told them to go away and come back when they were sober, but he feared that they would not come back, and he grieved over them; he felt that they were drifting away, but that they would always know the drag at the heart, and that wherever they went, whatever they did, whenever anything touched them, be it a glass of beer or "Star of the Sea" played on a barrel organ, they would be homesick.

Half an hour passed, an hour, an hour and a half. Father O'Grady grew stiffer and colder. He was cramped in the tiny box and could not stretch his legs; the chair was hard and straight-backed. Little points of rheumatism in his shoulders, and in the back of his neck, first began to ache and then to burn. His head ached too, and the air ceased to be air, and became a cold, fetid stuffiness.

The penitents whispered the miserable little stories of sin, on breath that was rotten with garlic. The priest had to make repeated acts of faith that the murmurs of attrition, which caused such uneasiness in the pit of his stomach, also caused the angels of God to rejoice. "But then," he thought, "Almighty God in His Providence has given them no stomachs to turn."

He leaned towards each one, offering up the discomfort, the nausea, the boredom, because he knew that in these people Christ had His will. In them, on this Saturday night, He renewed the life of the whole world, in this little box, the impact of love between God and man happened again, the world kissed the holy wounded feet in the dust.

The priest thanked God that it didn't matter at all that his own soul was dry and his body aching; that it was only with an effort that he could concentrate on each confession, not letting his mind wander for a second, so that he would be obliged to ask some poor child of God to repeat something over again; that it was harder and harder as each one came to the end, to think of even the most obvious platitudes to whisper for their encouragement.

He knew that it wasn't himself that mattered, though since God chose it to be so, he had to be there, just as the clay made of earth and spittle that Christ chose to put on the blind man's eyes had to be there.

He was glad that he had the cramp, the headache, the rheumatism and the nausea, because he had nothing else to offer in co-operation with God's huge intent of love.

The Humanity of the Son of God is too big for men. It scandalizes them. That He should pour the waters of life over souls on their weekly bath night, that He should renew the life of the world, not only in the inspired, the saints, the prophets, but in the maimed, the halt and the blind, in the inarticulate, the uninspired, the short-sighted, the dogged Saturday night regulars; that on the night of the sharpening of physical life, of the heightening of human emotion, with its taking hold of the heart and its sudden pang of desire, He should quicken His own life, His own immaculate passion of love, in the hearts of sinners.

That He the Omnipotent, the Immaculate, the Eternal, should become part of Saturday night—that is too much for the littleness of men.

Half an hour, an hour, an hour and a half, two hours. The scuffling and bustling in the church had subsided.

There was silence now, so that the drifts of sound from the street came in, but they sounded far away, and inside there was only the inaudible whispering from the confessional, like the rustling of sleepy birds in the boughs of a great tree.

At last it was over. The last absolution given, the last kiss on the hem of Christ's garment, and Father O'Grady could go.

—From *The Dry Wood.*

ALL THROUGH
THE NIGHT

G. K. CHESTERTON

Jazz is jerking, jazzers reeling
All through the night.
Raucous saxophones are pealing
All through the night.

Din like all damnation dealing—
Yelling, banging, howling, squealing,
Suit this air when played with feeling
All through the night.

Noise that keeps the night clubs going
All through the night.
Fizz and cocktails always flowing
All through the night.

Showy women not worth showing;
Men well-known but not worth knowing—
Loudly their own trumpets blowing
All through the night.

Nought can stay their mad gyrations
All through the night
Or the latest chic sensations
All through the night.

Save alarming indications
That the local police-stations
Also stretch their operations
All through the night.

Woeful poet sit not weeping
All through the night.
Peace a wiser world is steeping
All through the night.

They that have our lives in keeping,
Digging, planting, ploughing, reaping,
Still retain a taste for sleeping
All through the night.

—From *Return to Chesterton.*

THE SALESMAN

LEO TRESE

Scarcely have I shucked myself of hat and coat when the door-bell sounds an imperious summons. Through the glass of the door I can see my visitor—a salesman by the looks of him, with a briefcase under his arm. That moment of leisure with my first pipeful of the morning will have to be postponed. There comes that twinge of impatience, always in evidence when God's Will collides with mine. Why do there *have* to be salesmen—why can't they let us do our ordering by phone or by mail? But with my hand on the doorknob, the twinge is subdued. It is a long time since I learned my lesson of courtesy to all comers, but the years have not dimmed that lesson's effect. . . .

   He was a little fellow, on the rotund side, and fire-extinguishers was his line. I didn't want any fire-extinguishers, and I did want to get away for my appointment—an important one with three other priests and a golf ball. I told him quite civilly that I wasn't interested, but he was the pesky kind: he was sure I never had seen anything quite like his product; couldn't he come in and show it to me? Father Vicinus had bought three of them and thought they were wonderful. It would only take a minute—

He was shot down in mid-flight. If he'd had any sense he'd have seen me poised for the attack: "Listen, didn't you hear me say I wasn't interested? I don't want any, so quit wasting your time and mine. Beat it, will you?" Only I'm afraid maybe it sounded worse than that. He turned away as the door slammed, and I watched him down the steps. It was then that I noticed the neat little patch on the back of his topcoat, and the run-down heels, and the overdue haircut. It was the little patch that got me—that and the grace of God, being as I'm not given by nature to generous impulses. So I shrugged off the golf date (it looked like rain anyway) and called him back and tried to give a reasonable facsimile of a gentleman by my apology. We sat down and he showed me his wares and I told him what we had and he agreed we were pretty well covered.

Then we visited, over pipe and cigarette. He lived in a neighboring state, with his wife and four youngsters. His wife was a Catholic and he himself was taking instructions, almost ready for baptism. (How I squirmed at that! He was a catechumen, and I, a priest, had ordered him off the premises!). We parted friends, he with a rosary which I somewhat sheepishly slipped into his hand. It was good to see him turn back at the foot of the steps, and smile. It *was* starting to drizzle. I decided to go over to the school; the children hadn't seen me in a week.

Well, it was easier after that to suffer the plague of phone and doorbell. Whenever my natural snappishness strained at the leash, I had only to conjure a vision of a wifely patch on the back of a coat. Candle salesmen, wine salesmen, vestment agents and soap peddlers—I turn up the corners of my mouth as I open the door for each, and invite them in before I ask their business. My time is God's time, and God's time is all for souls. This man with the briefcase may be some other pastor's good parishioner, using part of his hard-earned commissions

82

to support the Church and to send his kids to the parish school; this fellow with the order-book sticking out of his pocket may be another priest's convert, or he may be the wrong side of a mixed marriage; even this glib lad with the Masonic emblem is one of the lot of us for whom Christ died. Any one of them, or all of them, may be influenced for life by the impression they carry away of me, a man of God. So it's, "Come in. Sorry I don't need any, but sit down a minute, anyway, and rest yourself a bit." Courtesy is so *cheap,* so easy.

So easy? Maybe that's over-simplifying a bit. I can't honestly ever be too sure of myself, whether it's a stubborn salesman, or a pestiferous parent, or a child with a rosary to bless. I still find myself having to apologize to someone, at least twice or thrice a year. It's in periods of stress and strain that courtesy costs the most. School-opening time, Holy Week, the last week of Advent—such as these are the danger spots. And how it hurts to apologize, especially when I know that I am right and the other party is wrong, as, strangely enough, always seems to be the case. But the other party isn't a priest; the other party isn't the one expected to set the good example. And the other party doesn't need the discipline nor the penance of apologizing half as much as I.

It's funny, too, what strong friendships can be born of an apology. Last Christmas my nicest gifts came from two persons to whom I've made myself apologize in times past. Not that I'd recommend apology as a career. But certainly there's many a wound in the Mystical Body that could so easily have been healed by a word of honest regret; or better still, wounds that never need have happened if patience had been at her post.

My hand still is on the doorknob. It has taken me a long time to open the door, and my friend on the other side is reaching doubtfully for the bell again. So up, up with the corners of the mouth. He's earning his living the hard way, and maybe he's got a patch on the back of his coat.

—From *Vessel of Clay.*

FATE WORSE
THAN DEATH

OLIVER GOLDSMITH

When lovely woman stoops to folly,
　And finds too late that men betray,
What charm can soothe her melancholy?
　What art can wash her tears away?

The only art her guilt to cover,
　To hide her shame from ev'ry eye,
To give repentance to her lover,
　And wring his bosom is—to die.

T. S. ELIOT

When lovely woman stoops to folly and
Paces about her room again, alone,
She smoothes her hair with automatic hand,
And puts a record on the gramophone.

　　　　　　　　—From *The Waste Land*.

BYRON

There is a tide in the affairs of women
Which, taken at the flood, leads Lord
　　　　　　　　knows where.

NO PAEANS TO PEDAGOGUES

U. S. student songs stress sports and ivy; Europe's are heavy on nostalgia. None find anything to hail in studying.

American student singing has long been built around football. To foreign ears it may sound strange to hear institutions of learning requested to fight, struggle and conquer every Saturday afternoon, and the songs containing the requests may seem to strike a slightly morbid note when they suggest that the students should be willing to die in return for their education. *Mon Dieu,* is this really necessary?

Of course nobody has ever been asked, in song, to die for the "dear old Sorbonne." Continental students generally hesitate either to sing or to shout for their universities. It is hard to say exactly why, but "Fight bravely, Stuttgart" or "Roar, Oxford, roar" just wouldn't *sound* right.

If you take away the football motif, universities have very little need for encouragement from their students. Even the American songs, which are unique in their whole-hearted flattery of the alma mater, have very little to say about education itself. "Teach, teach, teach" is a rare cry, even among the most dedicated scholars. Rarer still are songs which claim educational pre-eminence: "Better educated men are we" would be considered on all sides a pretty spiritless boast. The closest I could find to this particular approach is the University of Hawaii song which commences, "Deans so true, we are back of you"— but it seems that the Deans are, after all, the football team.

Foreign students feel the same natural aversion toward serenading the fundamental purposes of their universities. And since they have nothing equivalent to emphasized athletics (and precious little rivalry of any kind between colleges), they are forced to search for other subjects to sing about. In the search, they have hit upon several devices which might prove handy to American students.

The antipodes, which is upside down in so many ways, offers a number of student songs which actually abuse the alma mater. Some lash out at the professors:

> *Perhaps they didn't teach us much,*
> *But they taught us all they knew*

sneers the Sydney University medical school song. Others deride the students themselves:

> *Some are hung and some are married,*
> *Some for years in jail have tarried,*
> *Still we all are members of the same*
> *old Varsity*

is how the official Sydney anthem salutes its distinguished graduates.

A similar sentiment is expressed in a New Zealand song. At its own estimate, one of the branches of the national university is a place where

> *A sterilized swot [grind]*
> *With a head like a knot*
> *Gets the drop on a mere human man.*

When the Australian anthems condescend to praise, their compliments carry a heavy load of irony. For instance:

> *And now God bless our land,*
> *Give the Varsity council prudence,*
> *And bless its noblest work on earth,*
> *The Melbourne Varsity students.*

Songs of this kind are likely to crop up anywhere, but only in Australasia are they dignified as official student anthems, to be perpetuated in annual student song books. In other countries, including this one, abusive matter is generally too Rabelaisian (and parochial) to find its way into print. Songs like "Don't Send My Boy to Harvard," which sound at first like healthy pieces of self-criticism, usually turn out to have been written by members of other universities, and as such must be assigned to a section of the boasting-cum-football tradition.

Many student groups have their own anthems, which tend to be official anthems written in medieval Latin, which have absolutely no visible connection with the schools concerned.

These tend to fall into two main departments: first, the ones that just remind you to drink while you're young, stay young while you drink, and generally enjoy your youth as much as possible, before cirrhosis sets in; and secondly, the more melancholy ones for later on in the evening, which lament the passing of student days in spasms of premature nostalgia, a sort of remembrance of things present. If the alma mater is mentioned at all it is in such a general way that the anthem could easily be traded from one university to another. The alma mater they describe is just a home of youth, an anonymous luxury hotel for the younger set, and a symbol of times that never more shall be (pom pom).

The French military academy at St. Cyr provides the closest thing I could find to a self-deriding European anthem. This one describes, among other things, how three St. Cyriens depart from Hell (*i.e.*, the Academy) and the Devil who is in charge there by way of the window. This is probably a routine reaction to the military life (equivalent to the English wail "I don't want to join the Army") and as such it belongs outside the usual student category.

Many student groups have their own anthems, which tend to be technical in a ribald sort of way. Schools of medicine are particularly fertile, and there are many boisterous songs about cadavers and unpredictable lady patients. A fairly venerable example is a Scottish one which culminates in the following chorus:

Oh, listen while we ask in common phraseology,
If you can tell me what's the matter with the lady's
cardiology.

Students of "beaux arts" are probably the second most musical, but because their work does not offer anything specific to sing about they usually concentrate on love; and this slides quickly into the unprintable, students being the young dogs that they are.

As well as the institutional anthems, there are a number of international student songs that you are likely to hear almost anywhere in Europe. The writers of these have had the wisdom to keep their stuff printable and on the whole they cover the old ground of youth and drinking pretty thoroughly.

Three songs can be taken to show how the process works. "Gaudeamus Igitur," still the most popular of all student songs, praises youth in general terms. "Vom hoh'n Olymp" recommends that as we are young, so let us drink. And the French song "Chevaliers de la table

ronde" completes the cycle of printable student experience: the singer dies of intoxication, is buried in a black shroud by the nation's four greatest drunkards, and is crowned posthumously as king of the drunks. End of student.

Some of the international numbers are in Latin (nineteenth-century Latin frequently, but still Latin); most of the others are in French or German. The only tune that still covers the *whole* of Europe (and parts of Asia) is the chant of the wandering scholars of the Middle Ages, "Lauriger Horatius." This has since turned up as "Tannenbaum" and more recently as "The Red Flag," so that everybody gets a chance to sing it.

It might be added parenthetically to this that some of the militancy which Americans expend on football songs goes elsewhere into songs of patriotic pugnacity, especially in those parts of the world where students are liable to be called on to fight before graduation. The line between student singing and ordinary singing is sometimes a shadowy one. In German beer halls, where the students link arms with the public to sing about *schnitzelbanks,* it is hard to tell where student singing ends and everybody else's singing begins. Many of the Continental anthems belong as much to the town as the university and nobody knows who is responsible for them.

Nowhere is this line more shadowy than in England, celebrated home of compromise. Oxford and Cambridge have no official songs of any kind, and a singing session at either place is likely to turn into a duel between Welsh folksongs and Scottish folksongs, with somebody in the corner trying to sing "Greensleeves."

At my own college in Oxford they used to sing a strange medley of barrack songs, West Indian calypsos and hymns. On top of these staples we had frequent snatches of Afrikaans songs from the Veldt and occasional representatives from the international set, such as "Boire un petit coup, c'est agréable," "Silver Dollar" and "Ich bin der Musikant" (which allows one the huge sport of playing non-existent musical instruments). I think this mixture is fairly typical.

If an Englishman feels any tug of loyalty to his youth, impelling him

to sing, it is more likely to be exerted by his school than by his university. Several English schools have anthems, the most notable being "The Eton Boating Song" and Harrow's "Forty Years On," both of which are believed to cause much unashamed weeping among tough military men in all corners of the globe. It would be too much to ask us to cry over our universities as well.

Left to their own devices, the English have a marked preference for repetitious songs—"There was an old man, who had an old wife, who had an old horse," and so on for hours. Three particular favorites among students are (1) "Lloyd George knows my father, father knows Lloyd George," ad infinitum, to the tune of "Onward Christian Soldiers"; (2) even more mysterious: "We're here because we're here because we're here because we're here" (phonetically "weah heah") to the tune of "Auld Lang Syne"; and (3) more reasonably: "Why are we waiting," repeated as often as necessary to the tune of "Come all ye faithful."

Canada seems to belong to the American sphere of influence. When asked about their singing habits, Canadian students respond with the usual leers and winks, which indicates that they dip pretty freely into the vast international supply of risqué songs that have somehow got around the world without benefit of print.

But they also have serious anthems in the American style. Alberta students request their alma mater to "Guide us on through battle gory," which gets us back to the fighting-dying frame of mind. Western Ontario proudly states that "This U. is our U.," an incontestable boast. McGill strikes a slightly more modest note, in a line that might reasonably be attached to many other college songs, to wit: "Great our affection though feeble our lays."

The American method extends as far north as "All Hail Alaska" and as far west as the aforementioned University of Hawaii. Since many of the women's colleges have vainglorious anthems, too, it is obviously impossible to associate such songs with football alone. But I have a feeling that if you abstracted the lions and tigers, the blue and the gold, from American student singing, the anthems would melt into each other as the European ones have done: songs in vague praise of youth, of ivy (the great American contribution), and of friendship, which could be transferred without alteration from one college to another. Then, if you turned them into Latin, eked them out with popular songs, and saved your best work until the ladies had left the room, you would have something approximating the European situation. What the devil, though, is the Latin for Whiffenpoof?

—From *The New York Times.*

92

NEPHELIDIA

ALGERNON CHARLES SWINBURNE

If your head whirls, stop reading instantly.

From the depth of the dreamy decline of the dawn through a notable
nimbus of nebulous noon-shine,
    Pallid and pink as the palm of the flag-flower that flickers with fear of
the flies as they float,
Are they looks of our lovers that lustrously lean from a marvel of mystic
miraculous moon-shine,
    These that we feel in the blood of our blushes that thicken and
threaten with throbs through the throat?
Thicken and thrill as a theatre thronged at appeal of an actor's ap-
palled agitation,
    Fainter with fear of the fires of the future than pale with the promise
of pride in the past;
Flushed with the famishing fullness of fever that reddens with radi-
ance of rathe recreation,

Gaunt as the ghastliest of glimpses that gleam through the gloom of the gloaming when ghosts go aghast?
Nay, for the nick of the tick of the time is a tremulous touch on the temples of terror,
Strained as the sinews yet strenuous with strife of the dead who is dumb as the dust-heaps of death:
Surely no soul is it, sweet as the spasm of erotic emotional exquisite error,
Bathed in the balms of beatified bliss, beatific itself by beatitude's breath.
Surely no spirit or sense of a soul that was soft to the spirit and soul of our senses
Sweetens the stress of suspiring suspicion that sobs in the semblance and sound of a sigh;
Only this oracle opens Olympian, in mystical moods and triangular tenses—
"Life is the lust of a lamp for the light that is dark till the dawn of the day when we die."
Mild is the mirk and monotonous music of memory, melodiously mute as it may be,
While the hope in the heart of a hero is bruised by the breach of men's rapiers, resigned to the rod;
Made meek as a mother whose bosom-beats bound with the bliss-bringing bulk of a balm-breathing baby,
As they grope through the graveyard of creeds, under skies growing green at a groan for the grimness of God.
Blank is the book of his bounty beholden of old, and its binding is blacker than bluer:
Out of blue into black is the scheme of the skies, and their dews are the wine of the bloodshed of things;
Till the darkling desire of delight shall be free as a fawn that is freed from the fangs that pursue her,
Till the heart-beats of hell shall be hushed by a hymn from the hunt that has harried the kennel of kings.

94

CONVERSION

G. B. STERN

I was down at my country cottage in the depth of winter; and the friend sharing it with me had also been my nurse during those war-time years when I nearly died of septicaemia and three major operations, and during my slow fitful convalescence after the destruction of my London home with all my possessions. For these reasons I had adhered to her with limpet closeness, and she had suddenly had enough of me. This was not in the least surprising; I had had more than enough of myself, but did not know how my chronic state of dependence could be tackled, nor even feel that I wanted to tackle it; preferring to continue with the insidious habit of calling for support and always finding it. What had happened, I asked myself piteously, what had *happened* to those who had so tenderly welcomed me back to life, lapped me with solicitude and surrounded me with their protection and concern—"nothing ill come near thee"—what had happened to them? They were changed, they were hard, they did not care, they were letting me down. . . . And here was Nan, of all people, going off for a week to stay with another ex-patient whom she loved better than she loved me (I daresay she did by this time), skipping off wearing her new suit; could you believe a friend or nurse could be so callous? For I had started a cold, not yet feverish but by the evening anything might have happened, and it was beginning to snow, and there would be nobody to look after me and attend to my multitudinous wants except old Nannie, over seventy, hating the country and entirely useless in any crisis, practical or psychological. It proved to be one of those dramatic colds that possess you wholly and completely, and by the evening I was indeed very feverish, and by the evening the snow was thick on the ground and the pump had broken and I had used up all my large masculine handkerchiefs, about twenty-two of them, and Nannie was nervous and alarmed, and we could not get the plumber, and the roads and fields and gardens were white and silent, and my pillows were hot and tumbled, and I was abandoned and desperately unhappy, and this might go on, would go on, for days and days and nights and days. . . .

From the vantage of now, with a normal sense of proportion at least partially restored, all these troubles could hardly count as real trouble at all; merely panic.

However, I had friends, intimate friends, living near by, a rather exceptional group to be found within a two-mile radius; the most stimulating of them, previous to my world "shattered in shard on shard," had been chartered to come and see me soon after lunch the next day. If I could somehow drag myself through the heavy sands of time until then. . . . "Laura can't turn up later than half-past two," I assured myself during an endless morning, "and if she stays for an hour and a half—I'll have the armchair put by the fire near the window at the other end of the room—we can have tea early; and when she goes, there'll be Nellie to look forward to!" I knew hazily that Marguerite, yet another of our group, the gayest, the most popular, was moving sometime that day into a house she had taken down here after a couple of years spent in London. Bridget, I thought, might probably be helping her to move in; Bridget would therefore not have time to drop in and see me till the day after; and Nellie would come straight on from there at about six o'clock today; but Laura who lived a little further away, Laura who (I chose to suppose) was fonder of me than the others, Laura would not be likely to be rushing to and fro between a furniture-van and the garden in all this snow. . . .

"Oh, she's over at Marguerite's, helping," said the Doctor, her husband, after he had assured me I had a cold, a heavy cold, a feverish cold, and must not dream of getting up; "they're having a great time, you can hear them laughing and talking half a mile away." And he added a few words in praise of Marguerite's high spirits and vitality.

And Laura did not come, and the light faded, and the shroud of snow glimmered with a ghostly whiteness.

At tea-time, still forsaken, I could no longer bear my solitary banishment from the little world where you could hear laughter and voices from at least half a mile away. I rang up. After a time Bridget answered, breathless and a little impatient at being even for a moment snatched away from the fun. Just able to control my sobs, but only just, I asked if Laura were not coming? "I'll see." She went off, and came back with a terse message that Laura would be along presently; I could sense exasperation across the line at such a dismal interruption.

Dismal—dreary—desolate—dejected—despairing. . . . My mind hollow and empty as a vault, I began to compile this list of dark, dim d's. After a pause for intensive thought, I added "deplorable" . . . and speculated which most nearly fitted my condition. And chose "desolate."

I should have chosen "deplorable." Or I might have added "damaged" to the catalogue, in slight extenuation of my ludicrous self-pityings, for undoubtedly some damage had been done by too long convalescence and anxious spoiling and these were the after-effects.

"Oh God, who in creating human nature didst wonderfully dignify it. . . ." I did not yet know, of course, that a Missal existed; nevertheless I began to feel ashamed as though I had actually been confronted by this challenge to my self-respect. Why had I capitulated on such sorry grounds when during real catastrophe, war and death and danger, I still had been able to maintain a perfectly normal standard of decent behaviour? To pull myself together, I first had to take myself apart . . . and found the process peculiarly unenjoyable. In fact, I felt I simply could not do it alone.

Presently I heard the front door, and Nannie's greeting, and fickle Laura's brisk step on the stairs. In she marched with a "Well, what's all this about?"—spoken neither in patience nor in tenderness.

And it was then that I answered, to my own intense surprise: "I'm going to join the Catholic Church."

It was no sensational conversion on a heroic scale, no "voice speaking through me." And if now, some seven years later, I quote from George Herbert as well as the Missal, it is because in trying to extricate one clear reason for it out of all that wool and muddle, it has occurred to me that the first and last verses of "Man" expressed as clearly as with a diamond cutting poetry on a windowpane, my transition from contempt at what I was, to pride at what perhaps I might become:

> My God, I heard this day
> That none doth build a stately habitation
> But he that means to dwell therein.
> What house more stately hath there been
> Or can be, than is man? to whose creation
> All things are in decay.
>
> Since then, my God, thou hast
> So brave a palace built, O dwell in it,
> That it may dwell with Thee at last!

Indeed and indeed, I needed to remember consistently and to some purpose that I had for my birthright a derivation and a destination. This undignified lapse into dependence on the charity of my fellow-creatures who did not wish me dependent, was simply not good enough. Yet again, how strange that not real sorrow, real loss, real pain and danger had brought me into the Church, but a series of minor disillusions.

The reason for my conversion? That I had to dive from the shore to save the body of myself already drowning in deep water.

And another reason: that if you are by nature a hero-worshipper, you must find a Hero.

> All which I took from thee I did but take,
> Not for thy harms,
> But just that thou might'st seek it in My arms.
> All which thy child's mistake
> Fancies as lost, I have stored for thee at home:
> Rise, clasp My hand, and come!

—From *All in Good Time*.

CHRISTMAS CAROL FOR THE DOG

SISTER MARIS STELLA

This is a carol for the dog
that long ago in Bethlehem
saw shepherds running towards the town
and followed them.

He trotted stiffly at their heels;
he sniffed the lambs that they were bringing;
he heard the herald angels sing,
yet did not know what they were singing.

With tail erect and tilted ears
he trotted through the stable door.
He saw the shepherds kneeling low
upon the floor.

He found Saint Joseph watching by
Our Lady with her newborn Boy,
and being only dog, he wagged
his tail for joy.

99

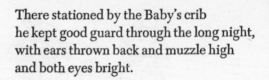

There stationed by the Baby's crib
he kept good guard through the long night,
with ears thrown back and muzzle high
and both eyes bright.

When the three tall kings came at last
he barked a warning to each one,
then took his stand beside the Child,
his duty done.

Down into Egypt went the dog
when Herod slew the innocents.
He was not wise. He did not know
why, whither, nor whence,

but only, being dog, he knew
to follow when the Family led
to Egypt or to Nazareth.
And no one said

a word about the sharp-nosed dog
who stuck close to the Family then.
And yet, there must have been a dog.
This is a song for him. Amen.

—From *Frost for Saint Brigid.*

100

THE SURGEON
AND THE NUN

PAUL HORGAN

Here you are. I haven't thought of this for thirty years. I don't know what called it to mind. I'll tell you anyway.

When I was a young doctor just out of internship I left Chicago to come West, oh, for several reasons. I'd worked hard and they were afraid my lungs might be a little weakened, and then besides, I've always been independent, and wanted to get out on my own, and I'd seen enough of the society doctors back there. Anyway, I came on, and heard of a new section of country in New Mexico, opening up, down toward Texas, and thinks I, I'll just go and see about it. The hottest day I ever spent, yes, and the next night, and the next day, too, as you'll see.

The railroad spur had been pushing down South through the Pecos Valley, a few miles a week, and it was in July that I got on the train and bought a ticket for Eddy, the town I was thinking about trying.

The track was completed all the way, by then, but they had a lot of repairing to do all the time, and no train schedule was maintained, because we'd move, and crawl, and then stop; baking; with nothing but dust to breathe, white dust like filtered sunlight; outside the car window was naked land—with freckles, I remember thinking: spotty bushes and gravel. Above, a blue sky like hot metal. The heat swam on the ground.

101

You couldn't sleep or read or think.

There was nobody to talk to in the car.

Two seats across the aisle from me was a Sister of Mercy, sitting there in her black robes, skirts and sleeves, and heavy starch, and I wondered at the time, How on earth can she stand it? The car was an oven. She sat there looking out the window, calm and strengthened by her philosophy. It seemed to me she had expressive hands; I recalled the sisters in the hospital in Chicago, and how they had learned to say so much and do so much with their skilled hands. When my traveling nun picked up a newspaper and fanned herself slowly, it was more as if she did it in grace than to get cool.

She was in her early thirties, I thought, plump, placid and full of a wise delicacy and yes, independence, with something of the unearthly knowingness in her steady gaze that I used to see in the Art Institute—those portraits of ladies of the fifteenth century, who look at you sideways, with their eyebrows up.

She wore glasses, very bright, with gold bars to them.

Well, the train stopped again.

I thought I couldn't stand it. When we moved, there was at least a stir of air, hot and dusty, but at that, we felt as if we were getting some place, even though slowly. We stopped, and the cars creaked in the heat, and I felt thick in the head. I put my face out the window and saw that we had been delayed by a work gang up ahead. They were Mexican laborers. Aside from them, and their brown crawlings up and down the little road-bed embankment, there was nothing, no movement, no life, no comfort, for miles. A few railroad sheds painted dusty red stood by the trackside.

I sat for ten minutes; nothing happened. I couldn't even hear the sounds of work, ringing pickaxes or what not; I felt indignant. This was no way to maintain a public conveyance!

It was around one o'clock in the afternoon.

Mind you, this was 1905; it isn't a wilderness any more out here. Oh, it was then. Every time I looked out at the white horizon my heart sank, I can tell you. Why had I ever left Chicago?

102

Then I wondered where the Sister was traveling to.

It was strange how comforting she was, all of a sudden. I had a flicker of literary amusement out of the Chaucerian flavor of her presence—a nun, traveling, alone, bringing her world with her no matter where she might be, or in what circumstance; sober, secure, indifferent to anything but the green branches of her soul; benign about the blistering heat and the maddening delay; and withal, an object of some archaic beauty, in her medieval habit, her sidelong eyes, her plump and frondy little hands. I almost spoke to her several times, in that long wait of the train; but she was so classic in her repose that I finally decided not to. I got up instead and went down to the platform of the car, which was floury with dust all over its iron floor and coupling chains, and jumped down to the ground. How immense the sky was, and the sandy plains that shuddered with the heat for miles and miles! And how small and oddly desirable the train looked!

It was all silent until I began to hear the noises that framed that midsummer midday silence . . . bugs droning, the engine breathing up ahead, a whining hum in the telegraph wires strung along by the track, and then from the laborers a kind of subdued chorus.

I went to see what they were all huddled about each other for.

There wasn't a tree for fifty miles in any direction.

In the heat-reflecting shade of one of the grape-red sheds the men were standing around and looking at one of their number who was lying on the ground with his back up on the lowest boards.

The men were mostly little, brown as horses, sweating and smelling like leather, and in charge of them was a big American I saw squatting down by the recumbent Mexican.

"Come on, come on," he was saying, when I came up.

"What's the matter?" I asked.

The foreman looked at me. He had his straw hat off, and his forehead and brows were shad-belly white where the sunburn hadn't reached. The rest of his face was apple colored, and shiny. He had little eyes, squinted, and the skin around them was white, too. His lips were chapped and burnt powdery white.

"Says he's sick."

The Mexicans nodded and murmured.

"Well, I'm a doctor, maybe I can tell."

The foreman snorted.

"They all do it. Nothin' matter with him. He's just play-actin'. Come on, Pancho, you get, by God, t'hell up, now!"

He shoved his huge dusty shoe against the little Mexican's side. The Mexican drooled a weak cry. The other laborers made operatic noises in chorus. They were clearly afraid of the foreman.

"Now hold on," I said to him. "Let me look him over, anyway."

I got down on the prickly ground.

It took a minute or less to find out. The little cramped up Mexican had an acute attack of appendicitis, and he was hot and sick and when I touched his side, he wept like a dog and clattered on his tongue without words.

"This man is just about ready to pop off," I told the foreman. "He's got acute appendicitis. He'll die unless he can be operated on."

The heat; the shimmering land; something to do; all changed me into feeling cool and serious, quite suddenly.

"I can perform an emergency operation, somehow, though it may be too late. Anyway, it can't do more'n kill him, and he'll die if I don't operate, that's sure!"

"Oh, no. Oh-ho, no, you don't," said the foreman, standing up and drawling. He was obviously a hind, full of some secret foremanship, some plainsman's charm against the evil eye, or whatever he regarded civilization as. "I ain't got no authority for anythin' like that on my section gang! And ennyhow, they all take on like that when they're tarred of workin'!"

Oh, it was the same old thing.

All my life I've got my back up over something no more my business than the man in the moon, but seems to me when it's a matter of right and wrong, or good and bad, or the like, thinks I, there's no choice but to go to work and fight.

That blasted foreman infuriated me. And I can swear when I have to. Well, I set to and gave him such a dressing down as you never heard.

I called him everything I ever heard and then I made up some more pretty ones for good measure.

I told him I'd have him up before the nearest district territorial judge for criminal negligence. I told him I was a personal friend of John J. Summerdown, the president of the new railroad, and I'd, by God, have his job so fast he wouldn't know what hit him. I told him that anybody'd stand by and let a man die instead of taking every chance there was to save him, I said was lower'n—Anyway, you can't go through medical school without picking up a few fancy words.

He cocked his elbows and fists at me a couple of times. But when I'm right, I know I'm right, and that's all you need to handle a peasant like that.

He got scared, and we both wiped the sweat off our brows at the same minute, the same gesture, and glared at each other, and I wondered if I looked as hot and messy and ignorant as he did, and I laughed.

The Mexicans were curious and asking questions and clawing at him. I turned around, like a nervous old maid, or a scared child, to see if the train was still there.

It had become a symbol of safety to me, the only way out of that yellow, yellow plain streaming with sunlight. Yes, it was still there, dusty black, and dusty white where the light rested.

The foreman talked to the men . . . there must have been about three dozen of them.

He may have been a fool but he was a crafty one.

He was talking in Mexican and telling them what I wanted to do to Pancho, their brother and friend. He pantomimed surgery—knife in fist and slash and finger-scissors and then grab at belly, and then tongue out, and eyes rolled out of sight, and slump, and dead man: all this very intently, like a child doing a child's powerful ritual of play.

"Oh, yo, yo, yo," went all the Mexicans, and shook their fists at me, and showed their white teeth in rage. No sir, there'd be no cutting on Pancho!

"You see?" said the foreman, "I told 'em what I had to do, and they won't have it."

I am no actor, and certainly no orator, but I turned to those poor peons and tried to show them as best I could how the only way to save Pancho, lying there like a baked peanut, was to operate right now.

You know? It was something like the old lyric struggle between good and evil—enlightenment and superstition.

There we were, miles from everything, on that plain where the heat went up from the fried ground in sheets; nothing but a rickety line of tracks to keep us in the world, so to speak; and a struggle going on over the theory of life or death, as exemplified in the person of a perfectly anonymous wretch who'd eaten too many beans once too often!

I'd be damned if I'd quit.

I went back to the train and had more on my mind now than chivalry and Chaucer and Clouet.

She was still sitting there in her heavy starch and her yards and yards of black serge.

Her face was pink with the heat and her glasses a little moist. But she was like a calm and shady lake in that blistering wilderness, and her hands rested like ferns on the itchy plush of the seat which gave off a miniature dust storm of stifling scent whenever anything moved on it.

I could hear the argument and mutual reinforcement in cries and threats going on and gathering force out there in the little mob. It was like the manifest sound of some part of the day, the heat, the desert life, which being disturbed now filled the quivering air with protest.

When I stopped in the aisle beside her, she looked up sideways. Of course, she didn't mean it to, but it looked sly and humorous, and her glasses flashed.

"Excuse me, Sister," I said. "Have you ever had any hospital experience?"

"Is some one ill?"

Her voice was oddly doleful, but not because she was; no, it had the faintest trace of a German tone, and her words an echo of German accent, that soft, trolling, *ach-Gott-im-Himmel* charm that used to be the language of the old Germany, a comfortable sweetness that is gone now.

"There's a Mexican laborer out there who's doubled up with appendicitis. I am a surgeon, by the way."

"Yes, for a long time I was dietitian at Mount Mercy Hospital, that's in Clefeland."

"Well, you see what I think I ought to do."

"So, you should operate?"

"It's the only thing'd save him, and maybe that'll be too late."

"Should we take him in the train and take care of him so? And operate when we reach town?"

Yes, you must see how placid she was, how instantly dedicated to the needs of the present, at the same time. She at once talked of what "we" had to do. She owned responsibility for everything that came into her life. I was young then, and I'm an old man now, but I still get the same kind of pride in doctors and those in holy orders when they're faced with something that has to be done for somebody else. The human value, mind you.

"I don't think they'll let us touch him. They're all Mexicans, and scared to death of surgery. You should've heard them out there a minute ago."

"Yess, I hear them now."

"What I think we'd better do is get to work right here. The poor wretch wouldn't last the ride to Eddy, God knows how long the train'd take."

"But *where*, doctor!"

"Well, maybe one of those sheds."

"So, and the train would wait?"

"Oh! I don't know. I can find out."

I went and asked the conductor up in the next car. He said no, the train wouldn't wait, provided they ever got a chance to go.

"We'd have to take a chance on the train," I told Sister. "Also, those men out there are not very nice about it. Maybe if you came out?"

At that she did hesitate a little; just a moment; probably the fraction it takes a celibate lady to adjust her apprehensions over the things she has heard about men, all of them, the very authors of sin, ancestors of misery, and custodians of the forbidden fruit.

"It would have been more convenient," I said, "if I'd never got off the train. That groaning little animal would die, and when the train went, we'd be on it; but we cannot play innocent now. The Mexican means nothing to me. Life is not that personal to a doctor. But if there's a chance to save it, you have to do it, I suppose."

Her response to this was splendid. She flushed and gave me a terrific look, full of rebuke and annoyance at my flippancy. She gathered her great serge folds up in handfuls and went down the car walking angrily. I followed her and together we went over to the shed. The sunlight made her weep a little and blink.

The men were by now sweating with righteous fury. Their fascinating language clattered and threatened. Pancho was an unpleasant sight, sick and uncontrolled. The heat was unnerving. They saw me first and made a chorus. Then they saw Sister and shut up in awe, and pulled their greasy hats off.

She knelt down by Pancho and examined him superficially and the flow of her figure, the fine robes kneeling in the dust full of ants, was like some vision to the Mexicans, in all the familiar terms of their Church. To me, it gave one of my infrequent glimpses into the nature of religious feeling.

She got up.

She turned to the foreman, and crossed her palms together. She was majestic and ageless, like any true authority. "Doctor sayss there must be an operation on this man. He is very sick. I am ready to help."

"W', lady," said the foreman, "you just *try* an' cut on that Messican and see what happens!"

He ducked his head toward the laborers to explain this.

She turned to the men. Calmly, she fumbled for her long rosary at her discipline and held up the large crucifix that hung on its end. The

108

men murmured and crossed themselves.

"Tell them what you have to do," she said to me coldly. She was still angry at the way I'd spoken in the train.

"All right, foreman, translate for me. Sister is going to assist me at an appendectomy. We'll move the man into the larger shed over there. I'd be afraid to take him to town, there isn't time. No: listen, this is better. What I *will* do: we could move him into the train, and operate while the train was standing still, and then let the train go ahead after the operation is over. That way, we'd get him to town for proper care!"

The foreman translated and pantomimed.

A threatening cry went up.

"They say you can't take Pancho off and cut on 'im on the train. They want him here."

Everybody looked at Pancho. He was like a little monkey with eyes screwed shut and leaking tears.

The little corpus of man never loses its mystery, even to a doctor, I suppose. What it is, we are; what we are, must serve it; in anyone. My professor of surgery used to say, "Hold back your pity till after the operation. You'll work better, and then the patient will be flattered to have it, and it might show up in the bill."

"Very well, we'll operate here. Sister, are you willing to help me? It'll mean staying here till tomorrow's train."

"Ja, doctor, of course."

I turned to the foreman.

"Tell them."

He shrugged and began to address them again.

They answered him, and he slapped his knee and h'yucked a kind of hound dog laugh in his throat and said to us,

"W', if you go ahaid, these Messicans here say *they'll sure 'nough kill you if you kill Pancho!*"

Yes, it was worse than I could have expected.

This was like being turned loose among savages.

You might have thought the searing heat of that light steel sky had got everybody into fanciful ways.

"Why, that's ridiculous!" I said to him. "He's nearly dead now! Osler himself might not save him! Nobody can ever guarantee an operation, but I can certainly guarantee that that man will die unless I take this one chance!"

"W', I dunno. See? That's what they *said* . . ."

He waved at the Mexicans.

They were tough and growling.

Sister was waiting. Her face was still as wax.

"Can't you *explain?*" I said.

"Man, you never can 'splain *nothin'* to this crew! You better take the church lady there, and just get back on that train, that's what you better do!"

Well, there it was.

"You go to hell!" I said.

I looked at Sister. She nodded indignantly at me, and then smiled, sideways, that same sly look between her cheek and her lens, which she never meant that way; but from years of convent discretion she had come to perceive things obliquely and tell of them in whispers with many sibilants.

"Come on, we'll move him. Get some help there."

The Mexicans wouldn't budge. They stood in the way.

"Give me your pistol!"

The foreman handed it over. We soon got Pancho moved.

Sister helped me to carry him.

She was strong. I think she must have been a farm girl from one of the German communities of the Middle West somewhere. She knew how to work, the way to lift, where her hands would do the most good. Her heavy thick robes dragged in the dust. We went into the tool shed and it was like strolling into a furnace.

I hurried back to the train and got my bags and then went back again for hers. I never figured out how she could travel with so little and be so clean and comfortable. She had a box of food. It was conventional, in its odors: bananas. waxed paper, oranges, something spicy.

Aside from that she had a little canvas bag with web straps binding it. I wondered what, with so little allowed her, she had chosen out of all the desirable objects of the world to have with her and to own.

My instrument case had everything we needed, even to two bottles of chloroform.

I got back into the dusty red shed by flashing the foreman's pistol at the mob. Inside I gave it back to him through the window with orders to keep control over the peasants.

What they promised to do to me if Pancho died began to mean something, when I saw those faces, like clever dogs, like smooth-skinned apes, like long-whiskered mice. I thought of having the engineer telegraph to some town and get help, soldiers, or something; but that was nervously romantic.

It was dark in the shed, for there was only one window. The heat was almost smoky there, it was so dim. There was a dirt floor. We turned down two big tool cases on their sides and laid them together. They were not quite waist high. It was our operating table.

When we actually got started, then I saw how foolish it was to try it, without any hospital facilities. But I remembered again that it was this chance or death for the little Mexican. Beyond that, it was something of an ethical challenge. Yes, we went ahead.

I remember details, but, now so long after, maybe not in the right order.

I remember a particular odor, an oily smell of greasy sand, very powerful in the shed; the heat made the very dirt floor sweat these odors up, and they made me ill at ease in the stomach.

It was early afternoon. The sky was so still and changeless that it seemed to suspend life in a bowl of heat. The tin roof of the shed lowered a very garment of heat over us.

Faces clouded up at the window, to see; to threaten: to enjoy. We shook them away with the pistol. The foreman was standing in the doorway. Beyond him we had glimpses of the slow dancing silvery heat on the scratchy earth, and the diamond belt of light along the rails of the track.

The camp cook boiled a kettle of water.

Sister turned her back and produced some white rags from her petticoats.

She turned her heavy sleeves back and pinned her veils aside.

The invalid now decided to notice what was going on and he tried to sit up and began to scream.

Sister flicked me a glance and at once began to govern him with the touch of her hands, and a flow of comforting melody in *Deutsch* noises. I got a syringe ready with morphine. And the mob appeared at the door, yelling and kicking up the stifling dust which drifted in and tasted bitter in the nose.

I shot the morphine and turned around.

I began to swear.

That's all I recall; not *what* I said. But I said plenty. Pancho yelled back at his friends who would rescue him. It was like a cat concert for a minute or so.

Then the morphine heavied the little man down again, and he fell silent.

Then I shut up, and got busy with the chloroform. Sister said she could handle that. It was suddenly very quiet.

My instruments were ready and we had his filthy rags off Pancho. Sister had an instinctive adroitness, though she had never had surgical experience. Yet her hospital service had given her a long awareness of the sometimes trying terms of healing. In fascinated silence we did what had to be done before the operation actually started.

There was a locust, or a cicada, some singing bug outside somewhere, just to make the day sound hotter.

The silence cracked.

"He is dead!" they cried outside.

A face looked in at the window.

Now the threats began again.

I said to the foreman,

"Damn you, get hold of that crowd and make them shut up! You tell them he isn't dead! You tell them—"

I began to talk his language again, very fancy and fast. It worked on him. I never cussed so hard in my life.

Then I turned back and I took up my knife.

There's a lot of dramatic nonsense in real life; for example: my hand was trembling like a wet dog, with that knife; and I came down near the incisionary area, and just before I made the first cut, steady? that hand got as steady as a stone!

I looked at Sister in that slice of a second, and she was biting her lips and staring hard at the knife. The sweat stood on her face and her face was bright red. Her light eyebrows were puckered. But she was ready.

In another second things were going fast.

I once told this story to someone, and later heard it repeated to someone else. I hardly recognized the events as my friend described them, because he made it all sound so dramatic and somehow like a scene in the opera, grand and full of high notes. No, it seems to me that the facts are more wonderful than all the things time and playgoing can do to a person's imagination. The whole situation couldn't have been meaner; more dangerous from forces like dirt and stupidity, instead of forces like fate or fascinating Mexican bandits. There was the hazard, too, of my own youth, my inexperience as a surgeon. There was my responsibility for Sister, in case any trouble might start. There was the heat and a patient with temperature and no way to cool off boiled water in a hurry, and the dust rising through the cracks of the door and window and walls of the shed, as the outraged men kicked and shuffled outside. We could see the sheets of dusty light standing in the room's dusk, sliced from the gloom by a crack of that sunlight and its abstract splendor.

Oh, my surgery professor and my colleagues would've been shocked to see some of the things I did, and didn't do, that day!

I tried to hum a little tune instead of talk.

But now and then the noise outside would get worse.

Or the foreman would creak the door open and stick his varlet face in to peer.

Or the patient would almost swallow his tongue making a noise like a hot sleeping baby.

So I'd swear.

Sister said nothing all the time.

She obeyed my instructions. Her face was pale, from so many things that she wasn't used to—the odors, the wound, manipulation of life with such means as knives and skill, the strain of seeing Pancho weaken gradually; she was glassy with perspiration. Her starched linen was melted. There was some intuitive machinery working between us. Aside from having to point occasionally at what I needed, things she didn't know the name of, I've never had a more able assistant at an operation in all my long life of practice.

I think it was because both she and I, in our professions, somehow belonged to a system of life which knew men and women at their most vulnerable, at times when they came face to face with the mysteries of the body and the soul, and could look no further, and needed help then.

Anyway, she showed no surprise. She showed none even at my skill, and I will admit that I looked at her now and then to see what she thought of my performance. For if I do say it myself, it was good.

She looked up only once, with a curious expression, and I thought it was like that of one of the early saints, in the paintings, her eyes filmed with some light of awareness and yet readiness, the hour before martyrdom; and this was when we heard the train start to go.

She looked rueful and forlorn, yet firm.

The engine let go with steam and then hooted with the exhaust, and the wheels ground along the hot tracks.

If I had a moment of despair, it was then; the same wavy feeling I'd had when the train had stopped here a couple of hours before.

The train receded in sound.

It died away in the plainy distance.

114

Shortly after there was a rush of voices and cries and steps toward the shack.

It was the laborers again, many of whom had been put back to work on the track ahead of the engine, in order to let the train proceed. Now they were done. Now they were crazy with menace.

It was about four o'clock, I suppose.

Fortunately, I was just finishing up. The door screeched on its shaken hinges and latch. I heard the foreman shouting at the men.

Then there was a shot.

"Most sacred Heart!" said Sister, on her breath, softly. It was a prayer, of course.

Then the door opened, and the foreman came in and closed it and leaned back on it.

He said they sent him in to see if Pancho were still living. I told him he was. He said he had to see. I said he was a blankety-blank meddling and low-down blank to come bothering me now; but that I was just done, and if he had to smell around he could come.

I showed him the pulse in the little old Mexican's neck, beating fast, and made him listen to the running rapid breath, like a dog's.

Then he looked around.

He was sickened, first, I suppose; then he got mad. The place *was* dreadful. There were unpleasant evidences of surgery around, and the heat was absolutely weakening, and the air was stifling with a clash of odors. Sister had gone to sit on a box in the corner, watching. She, too, must have looked like a challenge, an alien force, to him.

He grew infuriated again at the mysterious evidences of civilization.

He began to wave his gun and shout that next time, by God, he'd fire on us, and not on them Messicans out yander. He declared that he, too, was agin cuttin' on anybody. He was bewildered and sick to his stomach and suffering most of all from a fool's bafflement.

He bent down and tried to grab back the meager sheeting and the dressing on Pancho's abdomen. He was filthy beyond words. I butted him with my shoulder (to keep my hands away and reasonably clean) and he backed up and stood glaring and his mouth, which was heavy

115

and thick, sagged and contracted in turn, like loose rubber.

Sister came forward and without comment, knelt down by the wretched operating table which might yet be, for all I knew, a bier, and began to pray, in a rich whisper, full of hisses and soft impacts of r's upon her palate, and this act of hers brought some extraordinary power into the room; it was her own faith, of course; her own dedication to a simple alignment of life along two channels, one leading to good, the other to evil.

I was beginning to feel very tired.

I had the weakness after strain and the almost querulous relief at triumph over hazard.

I'd been thinking of her all along as a woman, in spite of her ascetic garb, for that was natural to me then. Now for the first time, listening to her pray, I was much touched, and saw that she was like a doctor who thinks enough of his own medicine to take some when he needs a lift.

The foreman felt it all too, and what it did to him was to make him shamble sullenly out of the shed to join the enemy.

We watched all night.

It got hardly any cooler.

Late at night Sister opened her lunch box with little delicate movements and intentions of sociability, and we made a little meal.

I felt intimate with her.

I had a sense of what, together, we had accomplished, and over and over I tried to feel her response to this. But none came. We talked rather freely of what we still had to do, and whether we thought the Mexicans *meant* it, and whether the train crew knew what was going on, and if they'd report it when they reached Eddy.

We had an oil lamp that the foreman gave us.

When I'd get drowsy, my lids would drop and it seemed to me that the flame of the wick was going swiftly down and out; then I'd jerk awake and the flame would be going on steadily, adding yet another rich and melancholy odor to our little surgery.

I made Sister go to sleep, on her corner box, sitting with her back

116

against the wall.

She slept in state, her hands folded, her body inarticulated under the volume of her robes, which in the dim lamplight looked like wonderful masses carved from some dark German wood by trolls of the Bavarian forests . . . so fancifully ran my mind through that vigil.

I saw morning come, like a cobweb, on the little window; then steal the whole sky that I could see; and then just as a flavor of cool sweetness had begun to lift into the air off the plains, the sun appeared (rapidly, I thought, but then it was I, not the sun, whose fever hurried life along that day).

Early that day Pancho became conscious.

We talked to him and he answered.

He was enclosed in the mystery of pain and the relief of weakness.

When he identified Sister by her habit, he tried to cross himself, and she smiled and crowed at him and made the sign of the cross over him herself.

I examined him carefully, and he was all right. He had stood the shock amazingly well. It was too early for infection to show to any degree, but I began to have a certain optimism, a settling of the heart. It had come off. I began to think the day was cooler. You know: the sweetness over everything that seems to follow a feeling of honest satisfaction.

Then the crowd got busy again.

They saw Pancho through the window, his eyes open, his lips moving, smiling faintly, and staring at Sister with a child's wonder toward some manifest loveliness, hitherto known only in dream and legend.

In a second they were around at the door, and pushing in, babbling like children, crying his name aloud, and eager to get at him and kiss him and gabble and marvel and felicitate.

They were filthy and enthusiastic, flowing like life itself toward that which feeds it. They were, then, infection personified.

I shouted at them and made them stay back. I let them see Pancho, but from a distance of three feet.

117

He spoke to them, thinly, and they cried "Aiee!" with astonishment, and nodded their heads as if sagely, and blinked their eyes at me, ducking their little bodies in homage. They couldn't have been more friendly now. They went yes-yes, and my-my, and how wonderful to have such a man! and he is my friend, and so forth.

But their very presence was dangerous, for they kicked up the dirt floor, and they hawked and spat on their words, and I finally put them out.

The foreman's mood was opposite to theirs.

He was now surly and disgruntled that we had pulled it off successfully.

He knew, as I had known, that the Mexicans really would kill if Pancho died.

We had the unpleasant impression that he felt cheated of a diverting spectacle.

We watched Pancho carefully all morning; he grew uncomfortable as the heat rose. But then, so did we. It rose and rose, and the bugs sang, and the tin roof seemed to hum too, but that must have been dramatic imagination. I had all our plans made. When the noon train came along, we would flag it, and carefully move Pancho on board, and take him down the valley to Eddy, where he could spend two weeks in the company hospital.

Mid-morning, I stepped outside and called the men together and the foreman, and made them a speech. Now they had their hats off, listening to me. Their little eyes couldn't have looked more kindly and earnest. *Sure*, I could take Pancho off on the train. *Sure*, they wanted him to get well. *By all means* the señor medico must do what he thought best. So with a great show of love for them, I shook hands with myself at the little mob, feeling like a gifted politician.

The train finally arrived, and as it first showed, standing down the tracks in the wavering heat, it looked like a machine of rescue.

There was only one more thing there.

When we went to take Pancho on the train, the foreman refused to help.

"I won't he'p you," he declared. "I ain't got no authority t' move none of my men, and I won't he'p you."

I picked out two of the less earthy natives and they helped me to bring the patient on board the train. We carried him on a camp cot. It belonged to the foreman. When he saw that, he got so mad he threw down his hat and jumped on it. The dust flew. His fish-white brow broke into sweat. Then he came running to stop us. We barely got Pancho on the train in time, and the door closed and latched. It was a state of siege until the train went again. It must have been ten minutes. Fortunately I'd brought my bags on board the first thing, and Sister's.

We finally pulled out.

We looked out the rear window, and saw our desert hospital recede into the slow pulsing glassy air.

We could see the little figures, most of them waving.

Just at the last, one of them held forth his arm, and we saw a puff of smoke, and heard an explosion in our imaginations, and then heard the actual ring and sing-off of a bullet as it struck the rear of the car.

It was the foreman's farewell, the last, and futile, opinion of the ignorant.

The afternoon passed slowly in the train.

The heat and the dust were hard on everyone, and especially Pancho. I kept wetting down the cracks of the windows, and the doors, to keep the dust out if I could.

But soon the water was gone, and we had to sit there and hope.

We reached Eddy in the evening, and it was like a garden, after the endless plains and their sear life. We found green trees and artesian wells and fields of alfalfa.

There is little more to tell, and what there is, is not about Pancho, except that he made a recovery in the proper time.

It is about my saying good-by to Sister.

It seemed to me we had been through a good deal together.

Now we were going to separate, for she was taking a stage-coach from Eddy on down into Texas somewhere, and I was going to stay a few days and see my patient out of the woods.

So we said good-by in the lobby of the wooden hotel there, where she was going to spend the night.

Nobody knew what a good job I had done except Sister, and after we shook hands, and I thanked her for her wonderful help, I waited a moment, just a little moment.

She knew I was nervous and tired, and it was vanity of course, but I needed the little lift she could give me.

But she didn't say anything, while I waited, and then as I started to turn off and go, she did speak.

"I will pray for you, doctor."

"What?"

"That you may overcome your habit of profanity."

She bowed and smiled in genuine kindliness, and made her way to the stairs and disappeared.

Duty is an ideal and it has several interpretations, and these are likely to be closely involved with the character that makes them.

You might say that Sister and I represented life eternal and life temporal.

I never saw her again, of course, but if she's still alive, I have no doubt that she's one of the happiest people in the world.

MR. MANDRAGON THE MILLIONAIRE

G. K. CHESTERTON

Mr. Mandragon the Millionaire, he wouldn't have wine or
      wife,
He couldn't endure complexity; he lived the simple life;
He ordered his lunch by megaphone in manly, simple tones,
And used all his motors for canvassing voters, and twenty
      telephones;
    Besides a dandy little machine,
    Cunning and neat as ever was seen,
    With a hundred pulleys and cranks between,
    Made of iron and kept quite clean,

To hoist him out of his healthful bed on every day of his
      life,
And wash him and brush him and shave him and dress him
    to live the Simple Life.

Mr. Mandragon was most refined and quietly, neatly dressed,
Say all the American newspapers that know refinement best;
Quiet and neat the hair and hat, and the coat quiet and neat,
A trouser worn upon either leg, while boots adorned the feet;
    And not, as anyone might expect,
    A Tiger Skin, all striped and specked,
    And a Peacock Hat with the tail erect,
    A scarlet tunic with sunflowers decked—
    That might have had a more marked effect,
And pleased the pride of a weaker man that yearned for
    wine or wife;
But fame and the flagon for Mr. Mandragon obscured the
      Simple Life.

Mr. Mandragon the Millionaire, I am happy to say, is dead.
He enjoyed a quiet funeral in a crematorium shed,
And he lies there fluffy and soft and grey and certainly
      quite refined,
When he might have rotted to flowers and fruit with Adam
      and all mankind.
    Or been eaten by bears that fancy blood,
    Or burnt on a big tall tower of wood,
    In a towering flame as a heathen should,
    Or even sat with us here at food,
Merrily taking twopenny rum and cheese with a pocket
      knife,
But these were luxuries lost for him that lived for the
      Simple Life.

—From *The Flying Inn.*

HARRIET BEECHER STOWE
AND THE SOFA THAT ROCKED

ALFRED NOYES

Mrs. Aldrich must have been the only person in existence who had
seen Harriet Beecher Stowe drunk, and in fact she was unintentionally
responsible for that equally unintentional lapse. Mrs. Aldrich's account
of this historical event, as I heard it from her own lips, was inimitable.

It happened in the first days of her married life, when the Aldriches were living in a much smaller house called Rose Cottage. Here one afternoon the young bride was tremulously expecting a visit from the author of that world-famous book *Uncle Tom's Cabin*; tremulously, for Mr. Aldrich had told her that the conversation would probably be lofty, since Harriet Beecher Stowe at the age of ten had written a thesis *Can the Immortality of the Soul be Proved by the Light of Nature?* He also suggested that as the weather was very hot a claret-cup should be prepared. He was called away for the afternoon and would not return till dinner-time. To the recipe which he had given her for the claret-cup, the young hostess, wishing to do all possible honour to so distinguished a guest, added something from a curiously shaped bottle which she understood came from a Carthusian monastery. What could be more appropriate? Had not Mr. Matthew Arnold (also a recent visitor to Boston) written a poem on the Grande Chartreuse?

Mrs. Stowe arrived, looking wispy, frail, and (as Swinburne might say) "pale with bitter summer." Almost her first remark was "I'm *so* thirsty!" Instantly free from all fear of conversation about the immortality of the soul, the proud young hostess produced her beverage and poured out a full tumbler. It vanished rapidly. A second tumbler followed and, to Mrs. Aldrich's amazement, Harriet Beecher Stowe's conversation assumed a nautical turn. She asked why the sofa was going up and down, and said she would like to get into her berth and take a nap, "if only the ship would keep still." The hoop-skirt that she wore added to the nonchalant effect of her recumbent position on the sofa; and Mrs. Aldrich, who was expecting other guests, began to wonder what she could do about those white cotton stockings and flowery garter ribbons. There were attempts to cover the inebriated Mrs. Stowe, only to be met with indignant little kicks, and the remark: "I won't be any properer than I've a mind to be. Let me sleep."

Sleep, in fact, lasting until dinner-time, saved the situation, though alarm again assailed the young hostess when she heard her guest describe to Mr. Aldrich the strange dizziness which she thought "had been caused by the train journey."

—From *Two Worlds for Memory*.

THE FIRE

HILAIRE BELLOC

I

We rode together all in pride,
They laughing in their riding gowns
We young men laughing at their side,
We charged at will across the downs.

II

We were companions. We were young.
We were immortal—so we said. . . .
For that which in the heart was sung
Could have no commerce with the Dead.

III

Oh! We should live for ever!—Yes!
We were immortal—till there came
Command imposing loneliness
And an extinction of the flame.

IV

And now it's over . . . How it rains!
And now it's over. Though the gale
Gives as of old its gallant hail,
A-driving at the window panes.

V

Lord! How the business disappears!
The golden faces charged with sense
Have broken to accept the years.
And look! what comes to Innocence!

VI

The chosen pictures I retain
Shall perish quickly as shall I.
Only a little while remain
The Downs in their solemnity.

VII

Were they not here, the girls and boys?
I hear them. They are at my call.
The stairs are full of ghostly noise,
But there is no one in the hall.

VIII

The firelight sinks: a reddening shade:
I watch alone beside the fire:
The fire of my good oak is made:
Where is the flower of my desire?

IX

A canker caught it at the root:
A twisted stock: a barren Briar.
It withered. It will bear no fruit.
Where is the flower of my desire?

X

Absolve me, God, that in the land
Which I can nor regard nor know
Nor think about nor understand,
The flower of my desire shall blow.

—From *Sonnets and Verse*.

BALLADE OF KINDNESS TO MOTORISTS

G. K. CHESTERTON

O Motorists, Motorists, run away and play,
I pardon you. Such exercise resigned,
When would a statesman see the woods in May?
How could a banker woo the western wind?
When you have knocked a dog down I have pined,
When you have kicked the dust up I have sneezed,
These things come from your absence—well, of Mind—
But when you get a puncture I am pleased.

I love to see you sweating there all day
About some beastly hole you cannot find;
While your poor tenants pass you in a dray,
Or your sad clerks bike by you at a grind,
I am not really cruel or unkind;
I would not wish you mortally diseased,
Or deaf or dumb or dead or mad or blind,
But when you get a puncture I am pleased.

What slave that dare not smile when chairs give way?
When smart boots slip, having been lately shined?
When curates cannon with the coffee tray?
When trolleys take policemen from behind?
When kings come forth in public, having dined,
And palace steps are just a trifle greased?—
The joke may not be morbidly refined,
But when you get a puncture I am pleased.

Envoi
Prince of the Car of Progress Undefined,
On to your far Perfections unappeased!
Leave your dead past with its dead children lined;
But when you get a puncture I am pleased.

—From *The Coloured Lands*.

HE JUST COULDN'T STOP

Guest: This cake is wonderful, what there is of it. Er . . . plenty of it too, such as it is.

128

PART TWO

Of Childhood And Unrelated

Topics

WORDSWORTH WROTE THE FIRST LINE

Heaven lies about us in our infancy
But later on we lie about ourselves.

CHILDHOOD OF A MONK

HUBERT VAN ZELLER

I. First School

If length of time spent in the same school justifies writing about it, then my nine years at Downside give me the excuse I want. It is true that the excuse does not arise in the case of the only other school which I attended, because I was there for only a few hours, but I mean to write about it nevertheless.

My first school, the one which served me so briefly, was in Alexandria. It was a day-school. I was just seven when my name was printed on its lists, and I suspect that the reason for this early start in education had as much to do with getting me out of the house in the mornings and until three o'clock in the afternoon—for I was becoming a nuisance at home—as with the need to have me well grounded in classics and mathematics before my entry into Downside in two years' time.

Looking back, I feel that the whole of this opening experiment in school life was badly stage-managed. Had I been simply taken off one day after breakfast and put in a classroom with instructions to stay there until I was fetched in the afternoon—as if it was the most natural thing in the world—it might have worked. I would have been suitably subdued during the first few lessons, and would have asserted a naturally gregarious nature by about lunchtime. Instead there was talk, almost in a whisper and for weeks beforehand, of "going to school." It was looked upon as a venture (which indeed it turned out to be) and was treated *au grand sérieux*. I was rehearsed in the correct decorum to be observed towards authority; I was given textbooks, exercise-books, a blotter, and a rectangular wooden box which divided horizontally into two (if not three) parts and which contained pencils, pens, clips, nibs and rubber bands. I was told (all this long before the great day) that since the carriage would be taking me there each morning I would be wearing my indoor shoes, but that I would be taking my outdoor shoes as well—in case there were games or in case the other boys wore them. It was explained that I would be bringing my luncheon in a small wicker basket, and that I would not be eating with the rest of the school but apart, in another room, in the company of the lady who taught geography. But above all—and this was the real weakness in the preparation for my pre-preparatory school career—I was able to see that my mother was dreading it as much as I was.

Then dawned the day itself. My father in over-boisterous humour, and inclined to slap one's back. My mother smiling bravely, but looking the picture of misery. I, noncommittal, glad to be the centre of interest, but hesitating between the role of martyr about to be flung to the lions—which would mean a strong resolute face—and the possible wisdom of insuring against the future by exhibiting uncontrolled grief. Perhaps the thought that my father's bluff determination would be impervious to tearful demonstrations inclined me finally towards the more dignified part of martyr, for I set off (as I learned long afterwards) with an expression of calm resignation on my face. Considering that I was due to be back in the house shortly after three o'clock on the same day, my composure does not now surprise me. Nor, knowing what my mother was like, does it surprise me to hear that my father extracted promises that there was to be no ringing up the school during the morning to find out how I was getting on.

I do not remember anything about the look of the school, or about the grounds, or whether there were such things as a theatre and a gymnasium. Apart from the classroom in which I sat for my one sole lesson, and to which I was led by the lady who taught geography, all I can remember is the sound of a piano-practice coming through the open window from another part of the building. For once my visual memory is a blank, and I think I can account for this by the discovery which I made on arrival that it was a school for girls as well as for boys. I had not been prepared for this, and I regarded it as an affront. Psychologists would probably agree that surprise and indignation are quite enough to fill the mind to the exclusion of all other impressions. Certainly I recall little else, before the class began, than the feeling of having been tricked. A woman's place, I felt, was in the home, and if she needs must learn to read and write and cast accounts, let her do so in a region apart, with others of her kind, but not, Oh not, with men.

Consequently when placed at the side of a little girl who was sitting on a window seat (the desks were already allotted by the time we arrived, the new pupils forming an overflow line under the window), I was in no mood either to learn or to weep or to play the martyr. I wanted to show that this sort of thing would not do.

Fortune, as alas it so often does in the beginning, favoured me. The cord which hung from the upper windows was within easy reach, and to this I attached the little girl's plaits. In order to follow the subject and see the blackboard we had to sit diagonally on our crowded window-seat, so the undertaking presented no difficulty. I suppose there was some sort of scene when the bell went, because after a surprisingly short space of time I found myself in the carriage again—with my outdoor shoes, my luncheon basket, my schoolroom gear on my lap as before, and with the lady who taught geography at my side. Glad as my mother was to see me back, it was a mixed reception that I got on my return. My father, when he came home that evening, was at first furious. "Flung out," he shouted, "O my God, flung out on the first day." But he very soon calmed down, and was even, I venture to think, rather proud of my anti-feminist flourish.

The blotter and exercise books were put away, the pencil-box was

133

given as a birthday present (a rather dull one I thought) to a small boy called Bridge Snow who was a neighbour of ours, and the wicker basket came in useful for my roller skates. But it was not an auspicious beginning. Expelled at the age of seven.

II. Other School

Form One, the lowest class, was my *habitat* for all except French and German. For French I was attached to a form which was three stages higher on the list, and for German I was one of a small group which received separate tuition from an almost legendary figure called Herr Heronberger. All three positions in the curriculum suited me perfectly, and in each of them I would have been happy to remain for the rest of my school career. In fact had it not been for considerations of age, and the desire to have greater freedom for painting, I would probably never have moved.

Since classroom competition interested me hardly at all, and since I have never felt the least curiosity about the sheer mechanics of acquiring knowledge, I can remember little of what went on in the classes at which I assisted. This is only another way of admitting that I was shockingly lazy—bored equally by the grammar of learning and the whole silly business of marks. I can remember the masters, the boys, the smell of the nictating gas, the noise of the lawn-mower in summer and of the straining hot-pipes in winter, can recall the feel of the desk on one's knees when one pressed forward in a game of "taxi," can live again the agonies of trying to keep awake in Mr. Wylie's class, and the punishments. But I cannot remember what we did the whole time. . . .

On one occasion the subject proposed for our essay was: "Describe some incident from your past life which has really happened." In Form One we numbered some whose lives had been crammed with vivid incident, and we set to work with zest. Only one boy in the class chewed an idle pen, and this was all the more surprising because he had been born in China, had travelled with his parents in India and the Near East, and had finally come on to Downside from a school in

Switzerland. "Surely there must be *something* you remember happening," insisted Father Walter. No, apparently there was nothing. The rest of us stopped our feverish scratching with pen and ink, and turned round to look at this tall fair boy who sat at the back of the class and who could not remember any single incident of interest in the past. "Think, boy," urged Father Walter five minutes before the end of the period, "just *think*." Inspiration must then have come to the writer, for on the paper which he handed up when the bell went were the words: "Once my father's nose bled and he had to lie down." . . .

French, in that more advanced form to which I have referred, was taught by a succession of masters. To me the great charm of belonging to this exalted group lay in the fact that one never knew from term to term, or even from week to week, whom one was going to get next. The war, with its consequent shortage of masters, was responsible for this state of continual flux, and not until Dom Gregory Quinlan was reluctantly drawn from his retreat in the monastery did the form possess a master who showed any sign of staying. Thus during my first year, when presumably the pre-war modern language professors were censoring letters and acting as interpreters in government offices, we had one man who was sick out of the window into the quad, another who, though living in the village, used to come up to the school in a red dressing-gown to have his bath, and yet another who averred that he was being pursued by ladies in the pay of the Spanish secret police, and who, in order to scare away these foreign adventuresses, used to conduct his classes carrying a sword-stick. So of course it was well worth belonging to that particular class.

With the arrival of Dom Gregory came a temporary lull: excitement dropped sharply. But though we no longer enjoyed the constant change of method, we enjoyed, under Dom Gregory, an absence of method of any sort. He was much too good and kind for the particular group which he was expected to teach, and often I would be sent out to receive punishment which I richly deserved. In those days almost all offences were dealt with by the Headmaster, so I had frequently to explain my frivolous behaviour to a man whom already I admired and whom later on I frankly venerated. He was to be my Abbot for the first four years of my religious life, and when he died I felt that a great current of power had ceased to run through the wires of Downside's life. But at the time of which I write, Dom Leander Ramsay was still Headmaster of the school, and as such he had to listen to me and administer correction when I was sent out of class by Father Gregory. Here is a specimen of one of our interviews: the first part is representative of many such, the last a verbatim account as I remember it.

"Well, what is it now? Father Gregory?"

"Yes, sir; fooling, sir."

"And he sent you to me?"

"Yes, sir; I'm afraid so, sir."

"In the middle of class?"

"Well yes, sir; just now, sir."

"Very good. Go and fetch the weapon, and get it over."

The 'weapon' was the instrument, whichever it might be, of correction. On this particular occasion I fancy it was the cane. After the formalities had been observed and I got my breath back, the dialogue continued as follows:

"You should not fool in Father Gregory's class. He dislikes it, and his sister has written a book about Damien the Leper."

"Is it a good book, sir?"

"Not very. But her name is May."

"Is it in our library, sir?"

"Probably not, probably not. Because you see she lives in Chilcompton. And keeps chickens."

"Oh."

"And the frontispiece is a picture of Father Damien painted by a very famous Pre-Raphaelite."

"Is it like him, sir?"

"No."

Such, with its deliberate *non sequitur*, was the quality of Dom Leander's humour.

—From *Willingly to School.*

136

WHEN WE WERE VERY SILLY

J. B. MORTON

I

Slip-Slop,
Pippity-pop,
You're at the bottom and
I'm at the top,
I'm at the ——
I'm at the ——
I'm at the ——
TOP.

II

I've got a silk-worm,
A teeny-tiny silk-worm;
I call *my* silkworm
Theobald James.
But nursie says it's cruel,
Nursie says it's wicked
To call a teeny-tiny little
Silk-
Worm
NAMES.
I said to *my* silk-worm
"Oh, Mr. Silk-worm,
I'd rather be a silk-worm
Than anything, far!"
And nursie says he answered,
Nursie says he shouted,
"You wish you were a silk-worm?
You little
Prig,
You
ARE!"

III

Some one asked
The publisher,
Who went and asked
The agent:
"Could we have some writing for
The woolly folk to read?"
The agent asked
His partner,
His partner
Said, "Certainly.
I'll go and tell
The author
Now
The kind of stuff we need."
The partner
He curtsied,
And went and told
The author:
"Don't forget the writing that
The woolly folk need."
The author
Said wearily,
"You'd better tell
The publisher
That many people nowadays
Like hugaboo
To read."

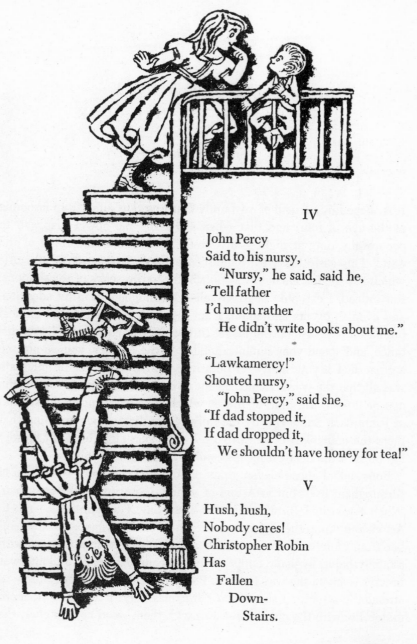

IV

John Percy
Said to his nursy,
   "Nursy," he said, said he,
"Tell father
I'd much rather
   He didn't write books about me."

"Lawkamercy!"
Shouted nursy,
   "John Percy," said she,
"If dad stopped it,
If dad dropped it,
   We shouldn't have honey for tea!"

V

Hush, hush,
Nobody cares!
Christopher Robin
Has
   Fallen
      Down-
         Stairs.

139

CHILDHOOD OF A
SCRIPTURE TRANSLATOR

RONALD KNOX

It is alleged by a friend of my family that I used to suffer from insomnia at the age of four; and that when she asked me how I managed to occupy my time at night I answered, "I lie awake and think of the past." This early habit of reminiscence must, I suppose, be the title which has singled me out as a contributor to this series of revisitations. For indeed, I can only boast myself a Birmingham man by adoption, and even so by fits and starts. I am a son of the manse, and clerical families are always on the move; further, if you go to school at a distance, and spend your summer holiday in the country, you do not see a great deal of your native, or putatively native town. Yet Birmingham was all that the word "home" meant to me from the age of four to the age of fifteen, the time of life at which that word means most; and as I approach Snow Hill by the railway the dingy brick arcading that faces the embankment still evokes, by the very sight of it, an illusory lightness of the heart; it means coming home for the holidays. . . .

Four out of those eleven years of my boyhood were spent not in Birmingham itself but at Aston, of which parish my father was vicar. When I revisited Birmingham the other day, I attempted a walk to Aston, and found the distance, unlike most of the distances we remember from childhood, too much for me. (I associate that journey with a family habit, hygienic doubtless but uncomfortable, of walking over in later years all the way from St. Philip's Rectory to Aston Church, to attend the afternoon service on Christmas Day. I associate it, more gratefully, with the old steam-trams with their broad cow-catcher, the engine a separate vehicle linked by a chain to the tram proper, which covered that distance at such a majestic pace in the nineties.) This time, I only got as far as the clock-tower that stands in the middle of the road, painted green now, though I think it was red in the nineties, the South Pole, in those early days, of all pedestrian expeditions. Aston, I hope, remains just as it was; the Vicarage garden with the big copper-beech tree and the brewery chimney overlooking it; Aston Park, with the trees, aged since then but surely not fallen, between which I played Tom Tiddler's Ground, and Aston Hall with the cannon-balls Cromwell shot at it, and the stuffed lion in the entrance, regarding new generations of children with the same glassy eye. If these things have changed, I would rather not hear about it. The people will have changed, but I don't remember them much. One went out to Gravelly Hill, to call on a Miss Morrison and a Miss Henn; one of them, I think it was Miss Henn, still played on the harp as a drawing-room accomplishment. On the other hand, I remember a Colonel Brody—was it Brody? some name like that—who kept a phonograph; an instrument which recorded the human voice on cylindrical rolls, and must have been the parent, I suppose, of the gramophone. Thus my musical memories of the period divide themselves into gracious contact with the past, and a horrible presage of the future. . . .

I cannot profess that my memories even of that restricted area, Birmingham proper, are photographically accurate. I have a bad sense of topography, and am probably the only person who even in youth, even on a dark night, has lost his way between St. Philip's Church and St. Philip's Rectory. That church and that rectory are the centre of all my associations; my father became rector there in 1895. The rectory stands at the further end of the churchyard; sandwiched, in those days, between the bank of England and the Bluecoat school, Mammon on one side and charity on the other, with an air of not letting its left hand know what its right hand did. I am sorry to find that the Bluecoat school has been pulled down, and that the window of my old bedroom is thus exposed to the profane eyes of Colmore Row, until they put up the monstrous hotel or whatever it is they are going to build there. I say I am sorry the school has been pulled down; for I remember it as a pleasant place in the eighteenth-century manner, with tailor's models of the inmates standing by the front door. But I am not really sorry that those boys are kicking their heels in the suburbs, instead of walking across solemnly, as they used to, to their pews in the gallery of St. Philip's every Sunday morning. The yard where I and my three brothers played was none too large for us; and our footballs were constantly having to be retrieved from the back premises of the Great Western Arcade at the back. The school playground was naturally larger, but it must have been a tight fit for the mob of boys whose shouts came to us over the side wall.

As for the church, it is outside what it always was; inside, they have taken out the pews and put in chairs and an extra Communion-table without, to my mind, creating in the least degree the illusion of a Cathedral. It was more of a piece as it was; those pews in which kneeling was hardly possible; those raised pews, best of all, at the back, for the Rector and the Wardens, where you were concealed from the public gaze when you were hunting for the threepence that had escaped through the glove that had a hole in it, but could peep over, comfortably, at the thrilling moment when the frock-coated sidesmen, re-united at last, began their solemn march, full-handed, up the nave. I suppose Burne-Jones' stained-glass windows are not really stained-glass windows, but what colour! And in those days, colour was the only thing that really mattered. . . .

Beyond Colmore Row was Barwick Street, where I learned to bicycle; the machine I used, family property, had only one tyre and that of solid rubber. (I think it was in Broad Street that I stared, round-eyed, at my first sight of a motor; but the traffic in Birmingham was already dangerous for an absent-minded rider like myself.). . . .

New Street Station afflicts me, even now, with a sense of vertigo, so often have I lost my bearings among its multitudinous platforms. My favourite memories are of Platform Four, I think it is, where I used to dodge the sham policeman who was supposed to take the bicycle tickets. I collected railway tickets in those days; and when you were returning

142

from a country ride to Lichfield or Kenilworth or Coventry or one of these jolly little country towns, it gave you a fine thrill to ride past at full speed, pretending deafness to his protests. . . .

I had nearly forgotten the football. Conscientious patriotism would take us, sometimes, to watch Small Heath (I think they call it "Birmingham" now) or even West Bromwich Albion, where they sold thick ham sandwiches and lemon cheesecakes on the ground. But primarily, of course, we were Villa fans; and I can still see the enormous advertisement of tyres which ran round the enclosure, "First in 1888, foremost ever since"—it was the year of my own birth, so I was apt to draw fallacious omens from it; still feel the panic of the human squeeze when you were swept out through the gates. Devey, and Athersmith, and Cowan, and Crabtree—I suppose those heroes of my youth now go unremembered. But I have stood on the seat, believe it or not, booing the referee when I suspected him of being unduly influenced by the claims of Liverpool; a feeling which seemed generally shared, though indeed claret-and-light-blue had the better of scarlet by five goals to nothing. That seems a long time ago.

Has Birmingham changed? Not much, I think; certainly not in its outward appearance; certainly not in its politics; certainly not in its air of cheerful bustle and tentative refinement. But man is the measure of all things; and in this case I am myself the measure by which Birmingham is judged. Could I really boo a referee nowadays? Could I still feel enthusiastic about the stuffed lion? It is a dreadful confession, but I feel as if it must be I, not Birmingham, that has changed.

—From *Literary Distractions*.

NAMEDAY

ROBERT FARREN

There! it is finished, the cake for your nameday:
brown, with red raisins, pink icing and candles,
fine, frilly red paper with podgy gilt puppies
to ribbon the rim like a wrist with its bangles.

To-morrow your quick little heart will start pounding,
your quick little laugh tinkle over the table.
As yet you're too young to suspect love abounding
went into that baking—later on you'll be able.

They'll heap you with names in the dear Irish fashion:
"Páistín," "little thrush," "peteen-o," and "heart's
    treasure."
Kind love will float round you, a pool of hushed passion:
you dear little soul, you'll be loved without measure.

Beginning the third of the years you are with us
the Father fulfil you, the Christ and the Spirit;
the Mother of Jesus be vigilant for us
nunc et in hora . . . and keep you, and cherish.

—From Selected Poems.

TO A SLIGHTLY OLDER BABY

G. K. CHESTERTON

This is the sort of book we like
  (For you and I are very small),
With pictures stuck in anyhow,
  And hardly any words at all.

. . . . . .

You will not understand a word
  Of all the words, including mine;
Never you trouble; you can see,
  And all directness is divine—

Stand up and keep your childishness:
  Read all the pedants' screeds and strictures;
But don't believe in anything
  That can't be told in coloured pictures.

—From *Return to Chesterton.*

F

CHILDHOOD OF A POET

ALFRED NOYES

I fear that I must be unfashionable enough to say that my schooldays were exceedingly happy, and in ways quite different from the usual picture. Once, for instance, when I was supposed to be studying Euclid I had hidden my Spenser behind an exercise book and was surreptitiously reading him (I had not yet been informed by Miss Edna St. Vincent Millay that Euclid alone knew beauty bare). Suddenly I felt the rap of some hard knuckles on my head, and heard a stern voice asking what I was reading. I handed over the book and was expecting trouble, when to my bewilderment Mr. Pope gave a little exclamation of pleasure, and held up the book to the rest of the class as if it were a kind of miracle. From my own point of view the miracle was that I escaped chastisement.

My ideas on the relationship between punishment and crime were further confused during a visit about this time to an austerely kind uncle. He was an extremely Low Church Anglican clergyman who used to preach in a black gown, and was described in an obituary notice as "a Puritan of the Puritans, holding the doctrines of John Calvin as embodied in the XVII Article of the Church of England. He was of the most gentle disposition and never dogmatic; but on matters of doctrine he would not be moved one hair's breadth." The only austerity I suffered personally was one which at this distance of time has a touch of Gilbertian humour about it.

My young cousin Herbert, while we were playing at Red Indians in the garden, hit me a violent blow on the head with his tomahawk. My gory head created a sensation when I ran into the house. My Calvinistic uncle, who had hitherto appeared to be detached from the things of this world, passed sentence upon Herbert: for an entire week he was to have no pudding at his midday meal. The following day was Sunday, when the Redskins were privileged to take that meal with their elders. Bandaged and complacent, I was looking forward to the moment when I could gloat a little over the spectacle of a hungry Herbert across the table. The great moment arrived. My aunt gave me a generous helping and I was about to begin when my uncle surprised me by saying: "Now, wouldn't you like to give an example of self-sacrifice?" Reluctantly putting my spoon down, I said "Yes"; whereupon my uncle handed my plate over to my still more surprised cousin. My aunt, all too kindly attributing to me angelic virtues, at once offered me another helping as a reward, but my uncle said firmly: "No. There would be no self-sacrifice in that."

I am afraid I did not appreciate his good intention at the time; for the little devil opposite (when his parents were not looking) waved his spoon about, licked his lips and patted his tummy, to indicate that he was enjoying himself immensely. And the sacrifice continued for the entire week. It was all a little confusing for me. My uncle was perfectly sincere and impartial; but I realized that if I had tomahawked my cousin I would have had the pudding.

—From *Two Worlds for Memory.*

147

A CHILD'S LAUGHTER

ALGERNON
CHARLES SWINBURNE

All the bells of heaven may ring,
All the birds of heaven may sing,
All the wells on earth may spring,
All the winds on earth may bring
    All sweet sounds together;
Sweeter far than all things heard,
Hand of harper, tone of bird,
Sound of woods at sundawn stirred,
Welling water's winsome word,
    Wind in warm wan weather,

One thing yet there is, that none
Hearing ere its chime be done
Knows not well the sweetest one
Heard of man beneath the sun,
    Hoped in heaven hereafter;
Soft and strong and loud and light,
Very sound of very light,
Heard from morning's rosiest height,
When the soul of all delight
    Fills a child's clear laughter.

Golden bells of welcome rolled
Never forth such notes, nor told
Hours so blithe in tones so bold,
As the radiant mouth of gold
    Here that rings forth heaven.
If the golden-crested wren
  Were a nightingale—why, then,
    Something seen and heard of men
Might be half as sweet as when
    Laughs a child of seven.

DADDY FELL
INTO
THE POND

ALFRED NOYES

Everyone grumbled. The sky was grey.
We had nothing to do and nothing to say.
We were nearing the end of a dismal day,
And there seemed to be nothing beyond,

THEN
Daddy fell into the pond!

And everyone's face grew merry and bright,
And Timothy danced for sheer delight.
"Give me the camera, quick, oh quick!
He's crawling out of the duckweed." *Click!*

Then the gardener suddenly slapped his knee,
And doubled up, shaking silently,
And the ducks all quacked as if they were daft,
And it sounded as if the old drake laughed.

O, there wasn't a thing that didn't respond

WHEN
Daddy fell into the pond!

—From *Daddy Fell into the Pond.*

CHILDHOOD OF A CARDINAL

MAISIE WARD

John Henry Newman, born February 21st, 1801, in Old Broad Street, was the eldest of six children. Charles Robert was one year younger, Harriett two and Francis four. Then came Jemima, born 1807, and finally Mary, born 1809.

When John was seven months old, his mother writes to her sister-in-law that "the little fellow's scarlet coat is come home—quite dashing —I long to see him in it." (Sending me this, his grand-nephew Mr. Mozley adds: "J. H. N. at some time, I believe, fancied himself a soldier, but it was another scarlet to which he was destined!")

Into a portfolio labelled "Autographic Remains No. I," Newman has pasted other memorials of his childhood. When he was four, a maid writes to his mother: "Marster Jon desires his deuty and wishes me to send you some violets." A year later comes a letter from his father which confirms Newman's own memory of being able to read perfectly at five.

My dear John Henry,
   This is the first letter your Papa ever wrote to his son. I request you will read it to your Mamma and Charles that, when he sees how well you can read writing, he will be very desirous of minding his book that he may also be able to do the same. But you will observe that you must learn something new every day, or you will no longer be called a clever boy.

I, therefore, hope that by next Thursday you will have got your Multiplication Table by heart and have also begun to learn your Pence Table. I mean to examine you as to your Multiplication Table and if I find you improve I intend after a time to buy a nice Copy Book and teach you to write.

The promise of a "nice copy book" was probably enticing to one who was to write incessantly for three-quarters of a century.

To the end of Newman's life memories of his childhood recur. Thus on a lonely birthday at Oxford he writes to his mother:

I woke on the morning of February 21, and, without recollecting it was my birthday, my mind involuntarily recurred to the day I was four years old, and said "The Cat and the Cream Bowl" [to a party of little ones in Southampton Street], and the day I was five years old your telling me that now I was a big boy, and must behave myself accordingly; to the day I was six years old, when I spoke Cowper's "Faithful Friend" at Ham.

A letter to his sister Jemima written in 1861 recalls this time:

I have lately been to see our house at Ham, which we had before you were born—where I was when you were born—and whence I sent my Mother by my Father the present of a broom-flower on your birth. 1 looked at the windows of the room where I lay abed with candles in the windows in illumination for the victory at Trafalgar. I had not seen them since I left in 1807. Those famous and beautiful groves are now in course of perishing—and in not so many years Dysart House will remain stripped and desolate amid its meadows.

The house is now fittingly a children's day nursery: the walls painted with gay frescoes, little blue cots for the afternoon sleep, a rocking-horse in almost every room (the Newmans had a rocking-horse to which John later sent his love from Oxford). It is a large square Georgian house with large square rooms, none of the nooks and corners common in country houses. Yet a country house it certainly is: you might be a hundred miles from London: you expect to meet a cow as you wander out into the paddock that lies at one side of the large neglected garden. Here are the shrubberies seen again in Newman's dreams. Here he went with Jason on the quest of the Golden Fleece or was turned to stone by the Gorgon: this garden was the scene for him of all the Greek legends.

At seven years Newman was sent from home to a boarding-school at Ealing having at first two hundred, later three hundred boys. His father had made a common mistake in urging forward a promising baby, for clearly he began at school as a child among boys. When his parents departed after their first visit, he was found by Dr. Nicholas in tears and urged to cheer up and join his companions.

"O, Sir," said the seven-year-old, "they will say such things! I can't help crying." Obviously he had escaped them to be alone. "O, Sir, but they will; they will say all sorts of things," and taking his master's hand he said, "Come and see for yourself." Only a baby could have done what he then did—led his master into the crowded room where, naturally enough, in his presence there was no teasing. But the story would seem to indicate a wide difference between Ealing and most schools of that or any period, if a homesick child of seven had nothing worse to put up with than teasing from a crowd of big boys.

No boy, Dr. Nicholas said later, had ever gone from the bottom to the top of the school at such a pace as Newman. An old diary records some of the landmarks of his progress:

> 1810, May 25   —Got into Ovid and Greek.
> 1811, February 11—Began verses.
> 1812, March 5   —Got into Diatessaron.
>   May 25   —Began Homer.
> 1813, May 3   —Herodotus.

It is good to note that the diary, kept with steadiness astonishing in a child, contains much else besides progress in his lessons. In 1810 the Christmas holidays produce "Had a twelf cake," "Went to see them scate," "Went to the play." Back at school he notes, "Had a whole holiday. Flew kite," "Made glass eyes to kite." Each day has a brief entry, even if it is only "rained" or "hot." "Had chicken pocks" is followed for ten days by the single word "ill." On another page is the rather pathetic entry, "Did no sums—could not get them to answer—ill."

An attempt at verse is made in the blank pages of the diary:

> Into the palace of the Lord
> Those who do right and keep His word
> Will surely go, but those who don't
> I am quite certain that they won't.

Not yet ten, he makes entries in Latin: "*Sum ire domum in minore tempore quam hebdomada. Huzza. Utinam irem domum cras.*"

The next year come the entries "Began music," "Began a tune." By 1812 he is "much better as to bowing," and his father writes: "If the Doctor approves of it, buy the Cremona." He "had paints," "went to see sailing match," "had greengages and pears," "had donkeys and cart"; and there are entries like "Dancing" (mentioned often enough to mean probably a lesson), "Conjuror came," "My birthday cake sent." June 5, 1812, has the pleasant entry, "Bathed—confirmation."

One summer holiday was spent at Worthing where they "went in a boat and bathed." The entry "Bathed" recurs constantly: at the seaside, at school, later on at Oxford—even in winter. Newman adds, in his Oxford days, the note that the cold bath at Holywell was a "plunging bath" but nowhere does he mention whether he could swim. It is the same in the life of Arnold: he also "bathed" constantly—but whether they just paddled in shallow water or struck out into the deep we are never told.

Into this volume of Autographic Remains are pasted several letters: among them the formal announcements of the holidays. In his journal he was writing "Huzza all this month at home"; in a very different exquisite copperplate he penned:

June 6th, 1810.

Dear Mama

I have again the pleasure to announce the approach of our vacation. It

begins as usual on the 21st instant when I hope to see you as well as it leaves,
Dear Mama,
your dutiful son,
John Henry Newman.
(All their lives his letters to his parents are signed "Yours dutifully.")

Although he bathed, went in boats and rode on donkeys, Newman was very far from being an athletic boy. He did not care for games and never played them. His amusements we can partly learn from these early papers. Scott's novels were just coming out and Newman, who had listened at home with delight to his mother's reading of "The Lay of the Last Minstrel," devoured the novels in bed in the early morning.

As he grew older the chief delight of his life was acting. The school put on a Latin play every year and he took a part in it. He hails this as the best event of the school year.

> Sweet is the notice that proclaims that all
> May lie in bed until a later call;
> Sweet is December first or first of June
> That shows the holidays are coming soon;
> Sweet is the hour that hails the incipient rule
> Of the new captain of our numerous school.
> But far more dear the glad auspicious day
> The doctor tells us we may have a play.

Newman himself wrote plays for his brothers and sisters. There was a "mock drama" of some sort in 1812 and "a satire on the Prince Regent." For a burlesque opera in 1815 he composed music as well as words. A separate note records "our home Christmas play," on January 10, 1815. The energies of all the family were thrown in. His father writes:

> The gentlest hearts the costumes have designed
> The nimblest fingers have its folds combined.

They were all musical and we find Mary later writing to her sisters about songs and scores, and daring to criticise Handel (the idol at that

154

period of the English public). She found him dull. Newman himself "attained," says Tom Mozley, "such a proficiency on the violin that had he not become a Doctor of the Church, he would have been a Paganini."

In spite of not playing games Newman attained a position of leadership among a group of boys. He started what was known as The Spy Club. To this belonged the three sons of the American Minister, John Quincy Adams, and the eldest of these named their periodical *The Portfolio*. It ran through twenty numbers and the Minister contributed to it. Newman was already writing two periodicals called *Spy* and *Anti-Spy*, written against one another, thirty numbers of one and twenty-seven of the other.

Spy [his brother Frank says] may have been his translation of "spectator": but many of the boys were made sore by the title, and told me that he *quizzed* everybody. Gradually it leaked out that he had initiated a number of the boys into a special Order, with whom he was every week to read *The Spy*. Among these was my second brother, but I, no doubt, was too young. Charles told me that there were degrees in the Order, marked by ribbons of different colours, with J. H. N. as Grand Master. The society met in one of the vacant rooms of this large school—I think afterwards the French master's. But indignation at the rumour of espionage soon culminated and the *profanum vulgus* of the uninitiated forced the door open, swept away the faithful officer on guard, seized the papers, and tore off the badges. Thus came the day of doom to *The Spy*.

—Condensed from *Young Mr. Newman*.

THE TOYS

COVENTRY PATMORE

My little Son, who look'd from thoughtful eyes
And moved and spoke in quiet grown-up wise,
Having my law the seventh time disobey'd,
I struck him, and dismiss'd
With hard words and unkiss'd,
His Mother, who was patient, being dead.
Then, fearing lest his grief should hinder sleep,
I visited his bed,
But found him slumbering deep,
With darken'd eyelids, and their lashes yet
From his late sobbing wet.
And I, with moan,
Kissing away his tears, left others of my own;
For, on a table drawn beside his head,
He had put, within his reach,
A box of counters and a red-vein'd stone,
A piece of glass abraded by the beach
And six or seven shells,
A bottle with bluebells
And two French copper coins, ranged there
    with careful art,
To comfort his sad heart.
So when that night I pray'd
To God, I wept, and said:
Ah, when at last we lie with trancèd breath
Not vexing Thee in death,
And Thou rememberest of what toys
We made our joys,
How weakly understood
Thy great commanded good,
Then, fatherly not less
Than I whom Thou hast moulded from the clay,
Thou'lt leave Thy wrath, and say,
"I will be sorry for their childishness."

HOW TO BE A DUNCE

G. K. CHESTERTON

The change from childhood to boyhood, and the mysterious transformation that produces that monster the schoolboy, might be very well summed up in one small fact. To me the ancient capital letters of the Greek alphabet, the great Theta, a sphere barred across the midst like Saturn, or the great Upsilon, standing up like a tall curved chalice, have still a quite unaccountable charm and mystery, as if they were the characters traced in wide welcome over Eden of the dawn. The ordinary small Greek letters, though I am now much more familiar with them, seem to me quite nasty little things like a swarm of gnats. As for Greek accents, I triumphantly succeeded, through a long series of school-terms, in avoiding learning them at all; and I never had a higher moment of gratification than when I afterwards discovered that the Greeks never learnt them either. I felt, with a radiant pride, that I was as ignorant as Plato and Thucydides. At least they were unknown to the Greeks who wrote the prose and poetry that was thought worth studying; and were invented by grammarians, I believe, at the time of the Renaissance. But it is a simple psychological fact; that the sight of a Greek capital still fills me with happiness, the sight of a small letter with indifference tinged with dislike, and the accents with righteous indignation reaching the point of profanity. And I believe that the explanation is that I learnt the large Greek letters, as I learnt the large English letters, at home. I was told about them merely for fun while I was still a child; while the others I learnt during the period of what is commonly called education; that is, the period during which I was being instructed by somebody I did not know, about something I did not want to know.

But I say this merely to show that I was a much wiser and wider-minded person at the age of six than at the age of sixteen. I do not base any educational theories upon it, heaven forbid. This work cannot, on some points, avoid being theoretical; but it need not add insult to injury by being educational. I certainly shall not, in the graceful modern manner, turn round and abuse my schoolmasters because I did not choose to learn what they were quite ready to teach. It may be that in the improved schools of today, the child is so taught that he crows aloud with delight at the sight of a Greek accent. But I fear it is much more probable that the new schools have got rid of the Greek accent by getting rid of the Greek. And upon that point, as it happens, I am largely on the side of my schoolmasters against myself. I am very glad that my persistent efforts not to learn Latin were to a certain extent frustrated; and that I was not entirely successful even in escaping the contamination of the language of Aristotle and Demosthenes. At least I know enough Greek to be able to see the joke, when somebody says (as somebody did the other day) that the study of that language is not suited to an age of democracy. I do not know what language he thought democracy came from; and it must be admitted that the word seems now to be a part of the language called journalese. But my only point for the moment is personal or psychological; my own private testimony to the curious fact that, for some reason or other, a boy often does pass, from an early stage when he wants to know nearly everything, to a later stage when he wants to know next to nothing. A very practical and experienced traveller, with nothing of the mystic about him, once remarked to me suddenly: "There must be something rottenly wrong with education itself. So many people have wonderful children and all the grown-up people are such duds." And I know what he meant; though I am in doubt whether my present duddishness is due to education, or to some deeper and more mysterious cause.

Boyhood is a most complex and incomprehensible thing. Even when one has been through it, one does not understand what it was. A man can never quite understand a boy, even when he has been the boy. There grows all over what was once the child a sort of prickly protection like hair; a callousness, a carelessness, a curious combination of random and quite objectless energy with a readiness to accept con-

158

ventions. I have blindly begun a lark which involved carrying on literally like a lunatic; and known all the time that I did not know why I was doing it. When I first met my best friend in the playground, I fought with him wildly for three-quarters of an hour; not scientifically and certainly not vindictively (I had never seen him before and I have been very fond of him ever since) but by a sort of inexhaustible and insatiable impulse, rushing hither and thither about the field and rolling over and over in the mud. And all the time I believe that both our minds were entirely mild and reasonable; and when we desisted from sheer exhaustion, and he happened to quote Dickens or the Bab Ballads, or something I had read, we plunged into a friendly discussion on literature which has gone on, intermittently, from that day to this. There is no explaining these things; if those who have done them cannot explain them. But since then I have seen boys in many countries and even of many colours; Egyptian boys in the bazaars of Cairo or mulatto boys in the slums of New York. And I have found that by some primordial law they all tend to three things; to going about in threes; to having no apparent object in going about at all; and, almost invariably speaking, to suddenly attacking each other and equally suddenly desisting from the attack.

Some may still question my calling this conduct conventional; from a general impression that two bankers or business partners do not commonly roll each other head-over-heels for fun, or in a spirit of pure friendship. It might be retorted that two business partners are not always by any means such pure friends. But in any case, it is true to call the thing a convention in more than the verbal sense of a collision. And it is exactly this convention that really separates the schoolboy from the child. When I went to St. Paul's School, in Hammersmith, there really was a sort of convention of independence; which was in a certain degree a false independence; because it was a false maturity. Here we must remember once more the fallacy about "pretending" in childhood. The child does not really *pretend* to be a Red Indian; any more than Shelley pretended to be a cloud or Tennyson to be a brook. The point can be tested by offering a political pamphlet to the cloud, a peerage to the brook, or a penny for sweets to the Red Bull of the Prairies. But the boy really is pretending to be a man; or even a man of the world; which would seem a far more horrific meta- morphosis. Schoolboys in my time could be blasted with the horrible revelation of having a sister, or even a Christian name. And the deadly nature of this blow really consisted in the fact that it cracked the whole convention of our lives; the convention that each of us was on his own; an independent gentleman living on private means. The secret that each of us did in fact possess a family, and parents who paid for our support, was conventionally ignored and only revealed in moments of maddened revenge. But the point is that there was already a faint touch of corruption in this convention; precisely because it was more serious and less frank than the tarradiddles of infancy. We had begun to be what no children are—snobs. Children disinfect all their dramatic impersonations by saying "Let us pretend." We schoolboys never said "Let us pretend"; we only pretended. . . .

It is time that something should be said about the masters. . . . Immensely important as we thought ourselves in comparison with those remote but respectable enemies, after all they did have something to do with the school. The most eccentric and entertaining of them, Mr. Elam, has already been sketched in brilliant black and white by the pen of Mr. Compton Mackenzie. I have forgotten whether Mr. Mackenzie mentioned what always struck me as the most disturbing eccentricity of that eccentric; the open derision with which he spoke of his own profession and position, of those who shared it with him and even of those who were set over him in its exercise. He would explain the difference between satire and the bitterness of the *risus sardonicus* by the helpful parable, "If I were walking along the street and fell down in the mud, I should laugh a sardonic laugh. But if I were to see the High Master of this school fall down in the mud, I should laugh a sarcastic laugh." I chiefly mention his name here for another reason; because he once vented his scorn for what he called "the trade of an usher" in the form of a rhetorical question addressed to a boy: "Why are boys sent to school, Robinson?" Robinson, with downcast eyes and an air of offensive virtue, replied faintly, "To learn, sir." "No, boy, no," said the old gentleman, wagging his head, "It was because one day at breakfast Mr. Robinson said to Mrs. Robinson, 'My dear, we must do something about that boy. He's a nuisance to me and he's a nuisance to you and he's a perfect plague to the servants.' " Then, with an indescribable extreme of grinding and grating contempt: " 'So we'll Pay Some Man. . . .' "

I say I introduce this ancient anecdote for another reason; and it is partly because I would suggest another answer. If ever the problem troubled me in my boyhood, it did not force me in the direction of the lofty morality of Robinson. The idea that I had come to school to work was too grotesque to cloud my mind for an instant. It was also in too obvious a contrast with the facts and the result. I was very fond of my friends; though, as is common at such an age, I was much too fond of them to be openly emotional about it. But I do remember coming, almost seriously, to the conclusion that a boy must go to school to study the characters of his schoolmasters. And I still think that there was something in it. After all, the schoolmaster is the first educated grown-up person that the boy comes to see constantly, after having been introduced at an early age to his father and mother. And the masters at St. Paul's were very interesting; even those of them who were not so obviously eccentric as the celebrated Mr. Elam. To one very distinguished individual, my own personal debt is infinite; I mean, the historian of the Indian Mutiny and of the campaigns of Caesar—Mr. T. Rice Holmes. He managed, heaven knows how, to penetrate through my deep and desperately consolidated desire to appear stupid; and discover the horrible secret that I was, after all, endowed with the gift of reason above the brutes. He would suddenly ask me questions a thousand miles away from the subject in hand, and surprise me into admitting that I had heard of the Song of Roland, or even read a play or two of Shakespeare. Nobody who knows anything of the English schoolboy at that date will imagine that there was at the moment any pleasure in such prominence or distinction. We were all hag-ridden with a horror of showing off, which was perhaps the only coherent moral principle we possessed. There was one boy, I remember, who was so insanely sensitive on this point of honour, that he could hardly bear to hear one of his friends answer an ordinary question right. He felt that his comrade really ought to have invented some mistake, in the general interest of comradeship. When my information about the French epic was torn from me, in spite of my efforts, he actually put his head in his desk and dropped the lid on it, groaning in a generous and impersonal shame and faintly and hoarsely exclaiming, "Oh, shut it. . . . Oh, shut up!" He was an extreme exponent of the principle; but it was a principle which I fully shared. I can remember running to school in sheer excitement repeating militant lines of "Marmion" with passionate emphasis and exultation; and then going into class and repeating the same lines in the lifeless manner of a hurdy-gurdy, hoping that there was nothing whatever in my intonation to indicate that I distinguished between the sense of one word and another. . . .

I am not sorry to be an exception to the modern tendency to reproach the old Victorian schoolmaster with stupidity and neglect and to represent the rising generation as a shining band of Shelleys inspired by light and liberty to rise. The truth is that in this case it was I who exhibited the stupidity; though I really think it was largely an affected stupidity. And certainly it was I who rejoiced in the neglect, and who asked for nothing better than to be neglected. It was, if anything, the authorities who dragged me, in my own despite, out of the comfortable and protected atmosphere of obscurity and failure. Personally, I was perfectly happy at the bottom of the class.

For the rest, I think the chief impression I produced, on most of the masters and many of the boys, was a pretty well-founded conviction that I was asleep. Perhaps what nobody knew, not even myself, was that I was asleep and dreaming. The dreams were not much more sensible or valuable than they commonly are in persons in such profound slumber; but they already had this obscure effect on my existence; that my mind was already occupied, though I myself was idle.

—From *The Autobiography of G. K. Chesterton.*

162

SCHOOL TEACHER

ROBERT FARREN

By the end of the first hour I am roaring and flaming
like a house-painter's blow lamp, striving to burn
    stupidity
like faded paint from woodwork; drudging, drudging,
saying it over, saying it over, saying it over.

"The soul of teaching is repetition."
        It was said urbanely,
and we scribbled it down, half-bored, in the teachers'
    college.
"Revision, repetition and recapitulation,
the indispensables of sound instruction."
        It was said urbanely.

He did not tell us, the man who had everything noted,
everything systematised, that it was torment.
He failed to say it was rain-drop, rain-drop, rain-drop,
beating and beating and beating on the forehead.

He spoke of "the backward child." He did not warn us
minds could hide below rocks, unblastable boulders
which detonating dynamite of purpose
could leave unscratched, with the midge intelligence
skulking there out of the daylight.
        I've set the road-drill,
the drill of my exasperated purpose
to bore through thick-ribbed concrete of stupidity,
and found that dulness beat me . . . I remember

rage filling head with hot blood, and (God preserve us!)
ecstasy spring from anger—so that a cringing
fear-stricken boy became a joyspring . . .
       Therefore I have run,
shuddering, from the chalk-dust. I have shunned
danger of my debasement.

       There is not,
in any lay mind soever, any conception—
there is not a beginning, a spark, a glimmering,
there is not a shadow of remote understanding
of the torture, of the bone-grinding agony
which is called in the text-books of education,
and in prim, annual sermons: This Grand Profession,
This Second Priesthood, Teaching.

—From Selected Poems.

POOR BANDAGED CHILDREN OF EVE

SISTER MARY JEAN DORCY

Clay is a fallible substance, heir to many blunders. It seems to tempt the Creator, Who so well remembers that we are dust, to bring down with a resounding crash anyone who tries to wear too much dignity. So often, like Peter, our words betray us.

Not that words well chosen and neatly fitted together cannot accomplish great things. Thought out discreetly and placed on paper they may be devastating in their effect. But on the stumbling tongues of Adam's children they often betray us and leave us in the spotlight with all the world laughing at us. Laughter is good for the soul, it is a great help to humility. Who can feel anything but humble, having tripped over the tongue in an attempt to say something very, very seriously? And what is of greater assistance in the matter of pulling "boners" than what Hamlet so feelingly calls "Words, words, words"?

Out of the mouths of babes have come some of the most heart-warming of blunders, without which the lives of teachers would be glum indeed. The pity of it is that teacher is so often allergic to anything like originality in her young charges. It's a disease she contracted in Normal School and it leaves its mark upon her for life. A child walks blank and unspoiled into her classroom, his mind open, his nerves sound. By every means in her power she strives to complicate his ignorance until he emerges from college a tattered wreck who no longer sees any possibilities in spelling and has lost all curiosity as to the native haunts of the least common denominator. Bound by iron-walled conventions he no longer trails clouds of glory, only gnat-like clouds of facts that will add to the annoyances of this harrowing existence: *i* before *e* except after *c;* 6✕6 is 36; the Spanish Armada was defeated in 1588. What a life! No wonder heaven is for children!

Children alone have the temerity to trifle with the rules that generations of unimaginative adults have laid down. "O my God, make Bismarck the capital of New Hampshire," wrung prayerfully from the heart of a hard-pressed fifth-grader seems no more impossible to the child (perhaps also to God) than some of the more stately petitions He gets from His college-level correspondents. But, grimly entrenched behind her substantial desk, teacher is dead set against such originality. Whether or not she wears a religious habit, she displays the same unbending loyalty to the silent *e* and the proper place for a comma, though it may take years of such teachers to stifle forever one's urge to spell by ear. By the time a youth is out of college he has had sixteen years of practice with the circumbendibus. He knows a dozen ways of saying a thing gracefully without letting anyone know what he is talking about. But lost—forever lost—is his childhood key to mystery, the direct approach. Life is real, life is earnest. He does not even care who

Ernest is any more. And nothing is as it seems, only as the statistical reports reveal.

Consider for one moment the joy of the direct approach. Forget, if you can, the rules of grammar and syntax and arithmetic with which you have blighted so many young lives. Pretend, if you haven't forgotten how, that you are nine years old. Shuffle off the garment of adult flesh. Return to the state of pristine ignorance where you thought Pennsylvania was large and pink, and Vermont small and lavender. Shed decimals, fractions, and compound interest, not to mention income tax. Breathe air uncomplicated by politics, philosophy, or afternoon teas. Look up at the world again, instead of down your nose at it. And there, under the spreading chestnut tree, the village blacksmith stands—of course you remember; Blessed John the Blacksmith and Blessed Michael the Dark Angel!

The ponderous words in which we clothe ideas in this never-too-graceful language so often betray us in our prayers. Here of all places we are dead serious; our poor mischievous mind is on its best behavior. It is no place for levity. Running a close second is the catechism with its completely sober statement of dogma. And yet, with this unpromising material, countless unsung urchins have developed private and hilarious heresies. The most brilliant heresiarchs in history have had to work much harder for results, and gave far less entertainment for their pains.

Some of the connections our children make are more intelligent than we are willing to admit. One prays earnestly, "Give us this day our day-old bread." Not money, not power, not quail-on-toast, but bread—specific, stale, solid day-old bread. It is something that we, shut from heaven with a dome more vast, would never think of asking heaven to give us. And how often we would be telling the truth if we just acknowledged, "O my God, I am *partly* sorry for having offended Thee—"

You've heard of Gladly—Gladly, the Cross-eyed Bear? It's an old story but ah—how quickly we forget its lesson! You can visualize it yourself; the stiffly-starched little girls, the cleaned-and-pressed little boys shined up almost beyond endurance, the Sunday-school teacher innocently

167

plunking out the accompaniment as her erring lambs bleat, with all the ardor of young hearts, "Gladly, the Cross-eyed Bear!" You can just bet on it that *she* has never thought of such a beast. She seldom thinks of bears, in fact, except bear and forbear, who probably are not cross-eyed. But to her unspoiled little satellites, a cross-eyed bear is just as good a subject for a hymn as a lot of other things people might name.

You learn very early that when a second-grader tiptoes up to your desk and enquires, "'Str, how do you spell AZZITIZZIN—you know, 'Str, I will be dumb on earth azzitizzin heaven?" it's no sign he has a drop of irreverence in his system. If he asks about the Forty Hours' Commotion, you take it calmly. He will just as fervently proclaim, "I plejja legion to the flag an tooth a repub brick where Richard stands; one ration in the visible with liberty and just as for all."

Dolores Whitney is one of those mythical people who exist only in words, like Richard who stands on the republic, life is Ernest, and sudden Sally. At least one child in every generation will get up the courage to ask who she is, and will hopefully repeat, "Hail Mary fulla grace Dolores Whitney" to see if you can identify her. Nobody means any harm by it but—words, words, words!

The call on a teacher's vocabulary was never greater. She has to have in her head a six-column polyglot edition of what are to her the simplest and most obvious truths, because her words and her children's may be centuries apart. You, for instance, give a dramatic rendition of the Flight into Egypt. Your rapt audience pictures St. Joseph phoning United Airlines, Our Lady packing airway luggage; while you trudge along piously beside the Holy Family across the burning plains of "Egypt's desert bleak and wild," your children have left you far behind and are already landing in Cairo. If you tell them emphatically that the angel told St. Joseph to take Our Lady and *flee* into Egypt, one of your budding naturalists will be sure to bring you the picture from her book and ask you, "If you pleathe, Thithter, where ith the flea?" You can't win.

A classic among the outpourings of uninhibited modern minds is this gem penned—it is sworn by the teacher—by a fourth grade boy:

THE FLIGHT INTO EGYPT

ACT I: *Bethlehem*

JOSEPH: *ZZZZZZZZ ZZZZZZZZ ZZZZZZZZ*
MARY: Zzzzzzz Zzzzzzz Zzzzzzz
JESUS: zzzzzz

ACT II: *Bethlehem*

ANGEL: Wakest thou, Joseph, you got to takest the Child and His mother and flee-est into Egypt.
JOSEPH: Wakest thou, Mary, we got to takest the Child and flee-est into Egypt.
MARY: Wake up, Jesus.

ACT III: *On the way to Egypt*

JOSEPH: Silent
MARY: Silent
JESUS: Silent

ACT IV: *Egypt*

JOSEPH: Look, Mary, those people are worshipping idols. Isn't that awful?
MARY: Look, Jesus, those people are worshipping idols.
Jesus looks
THE IDOLS: CRASH! BOOM! BANG!

THE END

While I have seen more than one play that would have profited by a third act like that, you can still see teacher's problem.

God's world is a never-ending source of awe to a child. Fascinated, he watches it unfold its mysteries—ripples in the water, baby ducks, a caterpillar. He is continually bumping himself against the world that man has made. Its furniture is too big for him, its jokes are not funny to him, and he is continually being rebuked for trying to make the

169

best of it. It is a bitter sort of betrayal to find that even words cannot be trusted.

God can be expected to understand all things, so it does not greatly matter that a child cannot, with his limited experience, realize the meaning of the words he uses. He will some day. We who are old enough to be mildly scandalized when a child takes undue liberties with an established formula of prayer sometimes forget that there are two sides to the question. We are the teachers, and it is certainly our business to see that the words he uses are the right ones, even if he does not at the moment understand all their meaning. But ours is the humbler office, after all. We deal only with the letter. It is theirs to teach us with what frank admission of dependence we are to plead our case to a God who can accomplish *anything* if He will. We tell a child dutifully that prayer is a lifting up of the mind and heart to God; *up* is a definite direction to him, and he logically looks *up,* higher than himself, for help. We are older, wiser; scientists have told us there isn't any up, so we measure God's greatness by our littleness, and our prayers do not soar very high at times. They can't; they are fettered to ourselves and to our limited view of what we, personally, think ought to be done. A child realizes that he has limitations—his report card is a standing testimony of it. There are lots of things he knows he doesn't know. To him, everyone from the child in the grade above him to the school principal and on up to God is wiser than he. When he needs help, he has the good sense to ask somebody for it. How many years has it been since we self-sufficient mortals remembered to do that?

Let us pray with the little English girl, evacuated from London during the blitz: "Dear God, take care of Daddy and don't let the bombs get him; take care of Mommy and don't let her be scared; and *for heaven's sakes,* God, take care of Yourself. If anything happens to You, WE'RE SUNK!"

May the divine sisters remain always with us, and may the souls of the faithful be parted, through the mercy of God dress in peace. Amen.

—From *Shepherd's Tartan.*

170

MR. DOUGLAS B. WATSON

ALBERT F. GRIFFITH

English 311b

When he says
The hills are like white elephants
You mustn't take it in the sense
Of literal meaning.
That is, he means there is a superficial
Similarity between the two that gives the backbone to his simile,
But not that the hills are textured
Like a pachyderm or even
Colored white by snow:
He means something subtle, simple, and (shall I say?)
Symbolic.
You see the point I'm driving at?
The hills
(You'll find he always makes the mountains mean eternity)
Are through subconscious substitution made to represent
The situation as the girl discerns it.
You see? You understand the implications?
The hills are something that can't be gotten rid of
And so's the situation—
And so you see:
White elephants.
You see? You do see? I hope you see.

171

RELIGION CLASS IN SCHOOL

LEO TRESE

As I stand outside the door of the eighth-grade room, it is, as always, with a sense of inadequacy that I await the sound of the bell which will signal the beginning of the religion period. Through the door's glass I can see forty-odd heads turned toward Sister as she explains square-root at the blackboard. Forty-odd heads which ought to know God better, forty-odd hearts which ought to love Him more. In a moment I shall go in for my weekly stint, and forty-odd voices will chant, "Good morning, Father," and forty-odd pairs of eyes will look at me expectantly; glad for the break in the monotony, not really caring much what I have to say.

Last week they were beginning their unit on the Church, and I talked about the Mystical Body. Since then they have been learning about the martyrs, so today I shall talk to them about the power of good example. With pointed questions I shall draw them on in the hope that they themselves may find the objective and enjoy the thrill of discovery. But I shall leave the room as I entered it, with a feeling of frustration that is saved from despair only by a consciousness of the potency of God's grace.

Forty-odd impressionable minds, forty-odd characters in the formative state, every one a potential saint or sinner. Dick there might easily go to the seminary and become an exemplary priest, or he might just as easily become a drunken bum like his Uncle George. Louise there—I can easily see her as the lovely Catholic mother of half a dozen kids, yet I know she may end up a selfish wench married to a divorced man. What will spell the difference, and how much of the responsibility will be mine?

Perhaps the heavy-heartedness is exaggerated today; Mrs. Borden's visit still is too fresh in my mind. She came in last night to tell me about

172

her daughter Eileen, married yesterday by a Methodist minister to a man who doesn't like priests. "And here's the medal she won right here in school, Father, the medal for Christian Doctrine." The poor soul was clutching it in her hand as though to prove that the whole thing was a mistake, a bad dream that would go away. Yes, I remember Eileen; she could always be counted on for the answer when everyone else was stymied.

Now where, *where* is the responsibility for the likes of Eileen, the too-numerous likes of Eileen? They spend eight, twelve, even sixteen years in the shadow of the altar, and then turn out to be spiritual tramps. Maybe the curriculum can take part of the rap: so many expertly designed courses that teach all the answers, but not how to live. The children use their missals at Mass with mechanical perfection, but have no vision of themselves as a part of the Bread that is being offered. (Some morning I should like to say Mass in the classroom, with just a table, a large one, for an altar, with the children gathered around and all receiving Communion. And then after Mass they would spread the table with the food they had brought for breakfast, and share their food together. Impractical of course, but what a lasting object-lesson it could be!)

But it's not for me to be belaboring the curriculum. I've not got enough credits in education to set myself up as an authority there. Much less shall I make scapegoats of the Sisters. Poor souls, with five and six subjects to prepare for each day, they do well to master the text itself, without being expected to give it the flesh and flush of life.

Well, if I skip the text and skip the teachers, that brings me right smack up against me! After all, I *am* the shepherd; they *are* my lambs. I may as well face it: when one of my flock goes wrong, there's something of me in the failure. When they crack under pressure, it isn't lack of knowledge that's responsible, it's lack of love. And love is not something that's learned out of books or at a blackboard. It isn't learned at all, it's imparted. It is a fire that is ignited by contact. I should never enter a classroom reluctantly, hesitantly, if my heart were bursting, as it ought to be, with love for Jesus Christ. I should never need to wonder what to say as I faced His little ones, if the pressure in my own heart were straining for escape.

How the Mass would stand out in the fourth dimension of Love! How the concept of the Mystical Body would rise living and breathing from the limbo of sterile imagery! How the distasteful duties of prayer and sacrifice would become, instead, challenges to divine adventure. Yes, it could happen here, it could happen now. All it takes is a holy priest, a saintly pastor. "And listen, Father T"—it's my Guardian Angel talking, and there are times I could gladly choke him—"listen now! Quit dodging the issue. Quit trying to whistle yourself by the cemetery. *Do* something about it, *right now!*"

The bell sets up its clamor, and forty-odd pairs of eyes swing from Sister to the door. Here comes mediocrity to teach perfection. I've got the picture now: a wavering and uncertain finger pointing to dim heights. I've got to clear my vision, and that bit of ocular therapy will have to begin at the knees.

Pedagogy has traveled far since my own boyhood. Today the eighth-graders are having a "socialized recitation." Joey is on his feet telling us about St. Lawrence, while all around the room others are rising and poising to supply the details that Joey will forget. One thing he doesn't forget: "Turn me over"—Joey is quoting St. Lawrence—"turn me over, I think I'm done on that side now." The kids appreciate the humor of the sizzling Saint, and there is a general chuckle as they look to see if I am enjoying it, too. I grin back, even as I wish that I had St. Lawrence's gift for discounting my own self-importance. There, I reflect, is a natural patron for moments of discouragement. Discouragement inevitably means that I am taking myself too seriously; always it accompanies that mood in which I seem to feel that I must save the world single-handed. . . .

A parishioner calls to tell me of a recently arrived neighboring couple who are married out of the Church. Maybe if I could call on them . . . ? The name and address go down on the desk pad, to be added to six similar ones awaiting attention. I sigh as I turn back to the task of drafting a raffle ticket for our forthcoming picnic. "Is this what I was ordained for?" I ask myself. Fifty per cent of my working hours spent at a desk, raising money, paying bills, listening to salesmen, writing letters, planning with contractors, supervising repairs, cranking a mimeograph and filling out forms? Nine-tenths of it a layman could do, and meanwhile there are souls to be saved on every side of me. Ernie Stein, for example. I read in last night's paper that he was married Saturday in the Baptist church. It's just a year and a half since I baptized Ernie, a promising convert. He broke up with his Catholic girl shortly after. Maybe if I'd followed him up a bit, kept in closer touch with him . . . ?

Right here is a good spot for St. Lawrence to step in: "Listen, my flurried friend," he says, "I may be only a deacon, but let me tell you a few things. What you're doing has to be done. Maybe a layman *could* do it, but just the same, if you don't do it, it won't get done. These desk jobs you moan about are part of your work, dedicated and made fruitful in your morning offering. Give God credit for a little sense. He knows how much time you've got, and He's made His plans accordingly. After all, two cents' worth of His grace can accomplish more than two gallons of your sweat; you believe that, don't you?"

By this time St. Lawrence has settled himself, with one foot on a chair, for what I can see is going to be a good lecture. "Just remember," he says, "that God's been in this business of saving souls a lot longer than you have. He's not asleep on the job, even when you seem to be piddling away your time running a movie projector for the Holy Name Society. The trouble with you, Father"—St. Lawrence wags his finger within an inch of my nose—"the trouble with you is that you're not so much interested in souls being saved as you are in *seeing* them saved; you want to be able to check them off as definitely present and accounted for. I can't reveal any secrets, but you may be surprised some day to find how many Protestants you prayed into Heaven without ever being able to include them in your annual report. Don't think that God is limited by the figures in the Catholic Directory."

My visitor pauses, but not for long: "Look at Father Harrumph," he admonishes, "he thought the job was too big for him, so he took to alcohol; and what good is he doing anyone now, in a sanitarium? Then there's Father Hustle, a chronic cardiac case, and Father Hurry with a nice set of ulcers; each thought that the world would go to pot if he didn't carry it personally on his shoulders. Now wait a minute"—Lawrence raises his hand to check my objection—"don't tell me about the saints who burned themselves out laboring for souls. When you're a saint I'll be willing to come back and discuss that with you. As soon as you start spending the whole night in prayer before the Tabernacle. . . . By the way"—Lawrence interrupts himself—"did you ever stop to think how much more fruitful your time would be if you did spend more of it in prayer, and less in running circles around yourself? Try that for a change. There's time enough to worry when a golf match means more to you than a convert instruction, or an all-night poker game more than your health.

"Well," Lawrence grins as he takes his foot off the chair, "I've been pretty serious, considering my reputation for a sense of humor. But just the same, don't forget what Marshal Foch said to his flatterers, 'Gentlemen, God could have done as much with a broken broom-handle.' There are far more worried priests than there are lazy priests, and I don't know but what the worriers dishonor God the more. . . ."

Eager snapping fingers recall me with a start. Joey has finished his recitation. As I clear my throat and dispel my reverie, I make a quick resolution: next time the appointment book is loaded and the day seems too short, instead of reaching for the baking soda, I'll just say, "St. Lawrence, pray for me!"

The morning's stint in school completed, I dawdle my way back to the rectory, still thinking about the children. They are a responsibility that weighs heavily. "Give me the child, and you can have the man." Hitler made it work—almost; the Commies seem to make it work; but do we? I'm not too sure. For a good many years now I've been talking glibly, like everyone else, about the children being our hope for the future. Yet the future, when it arrives, seems suspiciously like the past. And no one in all the wide world has such a chance at the children as do we priests.

There I go again, taking refuge in the crowd; talking about "we" and "us" when I should be saying "I" and "me." The only part of the world I'm going to have to answer for is right here within the boundaries of old St. Pat's. So far as I am concerned, the only youngsters in the world to be fashioned and formed are the kids in the little brick school on Exeter Road. Well, what am I doing to make them just a little bit better than their mothers and fathers? Not that their mothers and fathers aren't good enough, in an inoffensive sort of way. But a stranger would have a hard time distinguishing them from the mothers and fathers who got their start at the Lutheran school down by Sandy Creek, or from the mothers and fathers who learned their Bible lessons from old Reverend Merrill at the Methodist church-house. Week-days, they all seem cut to a pattern. They enjoy the same gossip, the same beer-gardens, the same trivialities.

If their offspring are going to be any different, I'm the one who will have to give them the boost, under God. It isn't that I don't know what the kids need. I'm quite sure that the doctrine of the Mystical Body, with its social implications for seven-day-week living, is the very dynamite they're waiting for, if only somebody—I mean if I could light the fuse. The trouble is, indoctrinating them in the truth of the Mystical Body, keyed to their level, would mean a powerful lot of work; a lot of study and meditation on my part. Shucks, the tract wasn't even in Tanquerey when I went to the seminary. I'd have to read the Encyclical, *Mystici Corporis,* and maybe two or three good books besides.

And it wouldn't end there. The Mystical Body would lead logically to the Liturgy. I'd feel that I had to read those bound volumes of the *Proceedings of the Liturgical Weeks* which have been gathering dust on my shelves, and maybe Pius Parsch and Abbot Marmion and a few others. There'd be results, of course. With the Mass come alive and the sacraments loved, the front pews might fill up first on Sundays; there might even be the lovely sound of many feet coming up the aisle on week days.

But I'm so *busy*. There isn't time for so much study and so much thinking; above all for so much thinking. But wait; let me be honest if nothing else. How about adding up the hours I spend skimming through the *Saturday Evening Post,* paging through *Life,* looking at the cartoons in *Collier's,* reading at least the "important" articles in *Reader's Digest,* not to mention my cover-to-cover consumption of *Time?* I tell myself that I must be well informed and abreast of the world, but in my lucid moments I have to admit that ninety per cent of what I read is hog-wash, forgotten within a week. It isn't information that I'm seeking, but escape; escape from the awful labor of thinking. All my so-called information doesn't even make for good conversation. Someone asks me if I've read such-and-such an article in the *Digest,* and I say, "Yes," and he says, "Oh," and that ends the discussion. If I say, "No, what's it about?" at once I'm a friend to him who is so anxious to tell me.

All right, I'll let my subscriptions expire. (As I tick them off on my fingers, I reflect that CARE can well use the money I'll save.) This next school year I'll start giving an hour religiously—in more ways than one—to the two upper grades. I'll study and master and teach the Mystical Body until those kids can see It move and breathe, and themselves a part of It. I'll make myself know the Liturgy as I should have known it years ago—its meaning and its power and its beauty. I'll get to love it with a love that I can pass on to the youngsters, until they'll be jumping in their seats with eagerness for it; fairly seeing the characters of baptism and confirmation shining through their ribs; praying the Mass and singing the Mass to make the windows rattle. I'll start off a generation that will stand out in this community as twenty-four-hour-a-day Christians. I'll . . .

I mean, I hope I will. But it would be so much easier to follow beaten paths. Why stick my neck out? After all, what the Ordinary requires and what the Confraternity Director imposes, should be good enough for me. The Sisters can teach the children better than I can; they're trained for it. Besides, I'll probably get changed about the time I'm nicely started . . . or else the whole thing will flop . . . or else . . Well, doggone it, I can *try. Deus me confirmet.*

—From *Vessel of Clay.*

WHERE *DO* FIREMEN GO?

Oh, my brother Bill is a fireman bold,
　　He puts out fires.
He went last night to a fire, I'm told,
　　He puts out fires.
The fire got into some dynamite,
　　Where poor Bill's gone we don't
　　　　know quite,
But, wherever he is, he'll be all right,
　　For he puts out fires.

MY CONVENT SCHOOL

I learned that it had been taken over by the Air Force, the big red-brick building—its long façade facing the road, the chapel jutting at right angles to its left, the Old House to its right—that had been the convent school run by French nuns in which I had been brought up from ten to eighteen years.

One day during the Second World War I motored past it, and I thought, in the glimpse I had of it, that it seemed not to have changed at all. Are houses wholly insensible to what happens inside them? Or do their atmospheres register events, making these live on in invisible warrings? I am inclined to believe the latter.

I remembered every yard of the buildings—the long corridors whose windows overlook the road and behind which were, on the ground floor, the refectory and music cells, on the first floor the class and recreation rooms, on the second the dormitories, and on the top the *greniers*.

In that flash I had seen the window where, on my way down one day from the *grenier* (whither, having a cold, I had gone to get a clean handkerchief but found the door locked), I had paused to peep through the muslin curtain at a regiment marching to its band. I did not notice that the German nun was approaching. That morning this nun, mounting guard over the girls' cold-water ablutions, had upbraided me for tying the arms of my dressing-gown round my waist, the better to get at my neck. I was fully dressed except for my uniform.

"Eileen Bussler" (my name was Butler), broke through the splashings, "you are *kvite* disgusting; you vash vitout your dressing-gown. You are *kvite* disgusting."

"Eileen Bussler," now broke through the martial music, "you vatch passing de soldiers. You vill lost all your marks for the veek."

180

"But, ba bère," I pleaded, looking up at my accuser and sniffing loudly because I was ashamed to show the damp rag that was my handker-chief, and putting into my voice all I could of appeasement, for I knew I had had high marks in class that week and stood a good chance of being top, "I only moved the curtain an *inch;* the soldiers couldn't see me, they never even looked *up*."

"Lower ze eyes, ples; you are too bold. You vill lost *all* your marks."

Does that German nun's spirit visit those long corridors now, I wondered? And what punishment does she wish meted out for the boldness of the blue-clad crowd that throng them now?

And what of the warrings in the atmosphere of the refectory? Do black-habited, white-capped ghosts flee with supernal swiftness into the corners, through the doors, out of the windows, to escape the sights and sounds of today's "orgies"? In those distant days each table was presided over by a nun who, with carving-knife and fork poised, asked each girl which of two dishes she preferred. It was an empty formula because of the unwritten law that the answer was always to be "Cela m'est égal, ma mère." Thus, if the choice was between roast pork, for which one had a relish, and slabs of leathery black liver, which one ab-horred, one had to say (with all the indifference one could put into one's voice, though one's eyes might dart involuntarily to the "crisp, tawny crackling") "Cela m'est égal, ma mère." And sure enough it would be the leathery liver. Or, if one was at the table presided over by the Mère Supérieure, who prided herself on her English, one would hear the query "Heggs or Heels?"; and while one knew the eggs (though pre-served in lime and tasting of it) were incomparably preferable to the black reptilian eels, one still had to answer "Cela m'est égal, ma mère." On Fridays there was served a thick green soup made of sorrel, and of a bitterness compared with which the psalmist's herbs would be as honey and the honeycomb. I *couldn't* swallow much of it without feeling I would most certainly be sick. I knew Friday was the day of special mortification; but this had nothing to do with being unmorti-fied; it was a sheer physical impossibility to go on. So, after a few gulps, I left it in my plate.

181

"Wat it is, ma petite? You feenish not dee good soup?"

"It makes me feel a little, just a *tiny* bit . . . not so well, ma mère."

"Ce que vous dites là est très malhonnête; c'est même *grossier*."

And the recreation hall? There must be many a major battle in its atmosphere, I thought.

Unhappily for me it had early been decided that I "recited beautifully." This meant that whenever there was *une Soirée* (attended by all the girls, which made your mouth dry; by all the nuns, which gave you the same feeling you have on a swing; by a priest or two, which made you feel you were giving way at the knees; and, very rarely, by a bishop, which gave you gripes) I was made to stand up and declaim. The piece I hated doing most, because I *knew* it made me look a fool, was "Spartacus to the Gladiators": I was about eleven when I was taught that one. With head well up, and white ribbon topknot (replacing, in honour of the occasion, the everyday plaits) vibrating with my nervousness, I would begin:

"Ye call me Chief." (Arms folded over thumping heart.) "And ye do well to call him Chief who for ten long years has fought upon the Arena" (arms unfolded and slowly extended) "every form of man and beast the broad Empire of Rome" (arms fully extended) "could muster, and who never once" (right extension brought slowly down to right side, left to left hip) "lowered his arm."

And what had become of the statue of St. Joseph which used to stand in the middle of the playing field—so benign, and which I was so afraid the hockey balls would hit? ("We *must* keep-up-wit-dee-times," the Mère Supérieure had explained when announcing the innovation of hockey.) Did an anti-aircraft gun stand in its place, pointing heavenwards as had done the lily in his hand?

And what of the warrings in the atmosphere of the dormitories? Did faint echoes of the "Benedicamus Domino" that jarred the girls out of their deep sleep at 6 a.m. make their way into the consciousness of the slumberers of today? And did the former terror of night air which forbade the opening of a chink of window, though fourteen or twenty slept in one room (thus producing a stuffiness which knocked you sideways when you returned with your clean linen from the *grenier*), take arms against today's airmindedness?

It was difficult to wake at 6 a.m., especially in the winter; but during the summer exams I would get a girl who was a miraculously early waker to call me at five, so that I could put in an extra hour's study. I must, I *must* come out top of my class and bring home a load of prizes weighty enough to make my adored father beam. Often the nun who came at six to rouse the dormitory with her clarion call would find me fallen sideways fast asleep with a book open on my knees.

The beds stood in a row, their heads to the wall, and were separated from one another by a space only wide enough to admit a chair. On these chairs, their backs also against the wall, reposed the underclothes the girls had worn during the day; and one night I made the quite appalling discovery that the new girl who occupied the bed next to mine suffered from the affliction vulgarly known as "Footman's Feet." Oh, horror, horror, *horror!* I had a very keen sense of smell; I leant so far out of my bed on the far side that I nearly fell out, and still my nostrils were assailed. Only when my head was right under the bedclothes could I steep my senses in forgetfulness.

Sometimes—generally at extra solemn moments, as when the striking of the hour by the big clock would break the silence of the preparation class and the nun who was taking it would chime in in sepulchral tones with a prayer for grace to pass this hour as one would wish to pass the hour of one's death—I would be seized with uncontrollable laughter. The thought of all these girls on their death-beds, all desperately intent on their lesson books—some frowning with concentration, some whispering the words to get them by heart, some stuffing their fingers in their ears to keep out a possible disturbing noise—was so comic that I shook and shook. It was apt to be contagious, and was an agony until the order "Sortez, Eileen, vous êtes un peu dissipée ce soir" gave me blessed relief.

This was the nun who was mounting guard at the foot of the stone staircase, down which the girls filed singly and in silence from the classrooms to the refectory, the day Hilda Magee missed her footing on the top of the final flight and slithered in a sitting position, and almost in tears from the pain, to the nun's feet. The command on that occasion was: "Remontez, 'Ilda, et descendez *convenablement,* s'il vous plaît."

And the chapel? In the fleeting glimpse I had had of it from the motor it had looked empty and unused. I hoped it was so, and that no warring elements disturbed its atmosphere. For the chapel was the centre and crown of the whole convent life. In it lived all beauty and love and consolation. There I would bring all my little offerings of hardships—Footman's Feet, and black liver, and tiredness, and sore throats, and algebra, and headaches, and feeling faint sometimes at early Mass and not being able to stop feeling so when the nun who was helping me out of the bench whispered "Courage, Eileen! Confiance dans le Bon Dieu," and the green soup, and the German nun—that seemed so infinitesimal when I thought of the wonder of God's love for me. When, after making the Stations of the Cross, I felt my heart would burst with love and grief, I would search my brain for some means of making up a little tiny bit for those immense Sufferings. Oh, I would turn *towards* the Footman's Feet tonight, eat no jam at tea today, and *next* Friday I would swallow *all* the green soup; I would be given enough strength to keep it down. I felt much consoled by these resolutions.

It wasn't all consolation in the chapel, though, for I was quite dreadfully troubled by scruples and searchings of conscience. The fact that the girls were always made to wear chemises in their baths, the fact that it was "quite disgusting" to wash, even though fully clothed except for your dress, with your dressing-gown lowered to your waist, *proved* that the body was wicked. The bits that showed were all right—say, from the top of your head to your Adam's apple at one end (I was glad about this, as I rather liked taking little peeps—I had to jump, as the rare looking-glasses were all hung too high for me—at my face), and from the soles of your feet to your knees at the other. And of course arms and hands, as you needed them for practically everything. It was the *trunk* which for some reason was so wicked. Pity, I thought, the trunk couldn't have been left *out* when we were being made.

The awful thing was that thoughts about the trunk *would* assail me. I tried with all my might to banish them, but the more I tried the more they seemed to come. I loved God so much—He *knew* I loved Him; but if I consented *wilfully* to one of these thoughts (*had* I consented? Oh, had I?), then surely I had committed a mortal sin? I knew the three conditions for a mortal sin—grave matter, full knowledge, and full consent. The first two were there—the wicked trunk and the knowledge that it was wicked. There was just a hope that my consent had not been quite full—that the indifference I thought I had momentarily felt might be just tiredness of my will from so much trying? The Catechism said: "Those who commit mortal sin crucify again to themselves the Son of God and make Him a mockery." Oh, *unendurably* horrible! . . . Terrible enough that that should have been done once long ago by men who knew not what they did; but that I who knew Him, whose Dearest Love He was, that *I* should make Him suffer that again! . . .

The lengthy penances I was allotted in Confession (having confessed to sins of whose real meaning I knew less than nothing) were, I felt sure, not nearly severe enough. Perhaps if I multiplied my voluntary mortifications sufficiently, those thoughts would keep away?

The chaplain, a thick-set Breton (I had a decided "pash" for him, and when, out of the corner of my eye, I saw it was he striding up the aisle my heart went pit-a-pat, and sank when I saw it was another priest), was also the Christian Doctrine and Scripture teacher. He had no use for newfangled forms of devotion, and constantly exhorted his pupils to use only the Church's ancient and majestic liturgy. After one of these exhortations I said to my class-mistress—an Irish nun with a sense of humour and therefore not likely to take it amiss—"I'm sure Père Patard has a great devotion to God the *Father*. God the Son would be much too modern for his taste and so would God the Holy Ghost."

In his sermons he frequently warned us girls of the dangers of the wicked world whose threshold we were approaching. The world was never mentioned by him without the prefix "wicked." I came to talk of it as the W.W. Would I ever be able to save my soul in the W.W., I who was so unusually prone to evil? Ought I not to become a nun? I would say nothing of this idea to any living soul. I would try a year in the W.W. and then I would know if I had a vocation or not. No use deciding on a life that brought you exceptionally near to the Feet of God if He didn't *want* you there. You *might* receive an Omnipotent Kick.

After a few months in the W.W. I was back in my beloved old school on a visit—very pleased to show off to the girls my pretty long frocks and my hair that was up. The nuns, relieved of the necessity for administering discipline, were able now to show their real kindliness. They buzzed round me. "Pourtant ce n'est pas très *eup*," laughed one of them, turning me round to see the heavy knot of hair at the back of my neck; they walked with me in the grounds, linking arms, and asking a torrent of questions about my new life. Even the German nun, though she neither buzzed nor linked, smiled sheepishly when I caught her eye. The Mère Supérieure, who invited me into her sanctum for a tête-à-tête, was a little worried that, in spite of a coming-out ball and other social launchings, I was not *fiancée*. In self-defence I confided I had had one proposal.

"You know, Eileen," came the swift warning, "soon you will fade like a little flower. And so you *meust* notte send them away at once. You must say: 'Ah well, you see, it is like ziss; I do notte know you, *beut—I will steudy you.*'"

Never had I felt more depressed. How awful, how quite frightful, if I was going to be a *complete* failure—spurned by the Feet of God for my unworthiness (or, which sounded much worse, vomited forth from His Mouth by reason of my lukewarmness, for already my ardour about the Religious Life had diminished) *and* overlooked by the eye of man because of my early wilting!

The study that was taking place there during the war was helping to drive the enemy from our skies. He was being sent away all right—if not quite at once. "O all you holy nuns looking down from above the stars," I petitioned silently as my car sped on, "pray that it may be soon and for ever."

—From *A Little Kept.*

LOUISA ALCOTT

G. K. CHESTERTON

It is very good for a man to talk about what he does not understand; as long as he understands that he does not understand it. Agnosticism (which has, I am sorry to say, almost entirely disappeared from the modern world) is always an admirable thing, so long as it admits that the thing which it does not understand may be much superior to the mind which does not understand it. Thus if you say that the cosmos is incomprehensible, and really mean (as most moderns do) that it is not worth comprehending; then it would be much better for your Greek agnosticism if it were called by its Latin name of ignorance. But there is one thing that any man can fairly consider incomprehensible, and yet in some ways superior. There is one thing that any man may worry about, and still respect; I mean any woman. The deadly and divine cleavage between the sexes has compelled every woman and every man, age after age, to believe without understanding; to have faith without any knowledge.

Upon the same principle it is a good thing for any man to have to review a book which he cannot review. It is a good thing for his agnosticism and his humility to consider a book which may be much better than he can ever understand. It is good for a man who has seen many books which he could not review because they were so silly, to review one book which he cannot review because it is so wise. For wisdom, first and last, is the characteristic of women. They are often silly, they are always wise. Commonsense is uncommon among men; but commonsense is really and literally a common sense among women. And the sagacity of women, like the sagacity of saints, or that of donkeys, is something outside all questions of ordinary cleverness and ambition. The whole truth of the matter was revealed to Mr. Rudyard Kipling when the spirit of truth suddenly descended on him and he said: "Any woman can manage a clever man; but it requires a rather clever woman to manage a fool."

187

The wisdom of women is different; and this alone makes the review of such books by a man difficult. But the case is stronger. I for one will willingly confess that the only thing on earth I am frightfully afraid of is a little girl. Female children, she babies, girls up to the age of five are perfectly reasonable; but then all babies are reasonable. Grown girls and women give us at least glimpses of their meaning. But the whole of the period between a girl who is six years old and a girl who is sixteen is to me an abyss not only of mystery, but of terror. If the Prussians were invading England, and I were holding a solitary outpost, the best thing they could do would be to send a long rank or regiment of Prussian girls of twelve, from which I should fly, screaming.

Now the famous books of Miss Alcott are all about little girls. Therefore, my first impulse was to fly screaming. But I resisted this impulse, and I read the books; and I discovered, to my immeasurable astonishment, that they were extremely good. *Little Women* was written by a woman for women—for little women. Consequently it anticipated realism by twenty or thirty years; just as Jane Austen anticipated it by at least a hundred years. For women are the only realists; their whole object in life is to pit their realism against the extravagant, excessive, and occasionally drunken idealism of men. I do not hesitate. I am not ashamed to name Miss Alcott and Miss Austen. There is, indeed, a vast division in the matter of literature (an unimportant matter), but there is the same silent and unexplained assumption of the feminine point of view. There is no pretence, as most unfortunately occurred in the case of another woman of genius, George Eliot, that the writer is anything else but a woman, writing to amuse other women, with her awful womanly irony. Jane Austen did not call herself George Austen; nor Louisa Alcott call herself George Alcott. These women refrained from that abject submission to the male sex which we have since been distressed to see; the weak demand for masculine names and for a part in merely masculine frivolities; parliaments, for instance. These were strong women; they classed parliament with the public-house. But for another and better reason, I do not hesitate to name Miss Alcott by the side of Jane Austen; because her talent, though doubtless inferior, was

188

of exactly the same kind. There is an unmistakable material truth about the thing; if that material truth were not the chief female characteristic, we should most of us find our houses burnt down when we went back to them. To take but one instance out of many, and an instance that a man can understand, because a man was involved, the account of the quite sudden and quite blundering proposal, acceptance, and engagement between Jo and the German professor under the umbrella, with parcels falling off them, so to speak, every minute, is one of the really human things in human literature; when you read it you feel sure that human beings have experienced it often; you almost feel that you have experienced it yourself. There is something true to all our own private diaries in the fact that our happiest moments have happened in the rain, or under some absurd impediment of absurd luggage. The same is true of a hundred other elements in the story. The whole affair of the children acting the different parts in *Pickwick,* forming a childish club under strict restrictions, in order to do so; all that is really life, even where it is not literature. And as a final touch of human truth, nothing could be better than the way in which Miss Alcott suggests the borders and the sensitive privacy of such an experiment. All the little girls have become interested, as they would in real life, in the lonely little boy next door; but when one of them introduces him into their private club in imitation of *Pickwick,* there is a general stir of resistance; these family fictions do not endure being considered from the outside.

All that is profoundly true; and something more than that is profoundly true. For just as the boy was an intruder in that club of girls, so any masculine reader is really an intruder among this pile of books. There runs through the whole series a certain moral philosophy, which a man can never really get the hang of. For instance, the girls are always doing something, pleasant or unpleasant. In fact, when they have not to do something unpleasant, they deliberately do something else. A great part, perhaps the more godlike part, of a boy's life, is passed in doing nothing at all. Real selfishness, which is the simplest thing in the world to a boy or man, is practically left out of the calculation. The girls may conceivably oppress and torture each other; but they will not in-

dulge or even enjoy themselves—not, at least, as men understand in-
dulgence or enjoyment. The strangest things are taken for granted; as
that it is wrong in itself to drink champagne. But two things are quite
certain; first, that even from a masculine standpoint, the books are very
good; and second, that from a feminine standpoint they are so good
that their admirers have really lost sight even of their goodness. I have
never known, or hardly ever known, a really admirable woman who did
not confess to having read these books. Haughty ladies confessed (under
torture) that they liked them still. Stately Suffragettes rose rustling
from the sofa and dropped *Little Women* on the floor, covering them
with public shame. At learned ladies' colleges, it is, I firmly believe,
handed about secretly, like a dangerous drug. I cannot understand this
strange and simple world, in which unselfishness is natural, in which
spite is easier than self-indulgence. I am the male intruder, like poor
Mr. Laurence, and I withdraw. I back out hastily, bowing. But I am
sure that I leave a very interesting world behind me.

—From *A Handful of Authors.*

GIRL GUIDES

G. K. CHESTERTON

When Cleopatra was made a Guide,
She let her militant duties slide,
And when her prattle had lost the battle
Tactfully tickled a snake and died.

When Boadicea was made a Guide,
Her visage the vividest blue was dyed;
So the coat was made of a similar shade
And she travelled on wheels with the spokes outside.

When Lady Godiva was made a Guide,
The uniform had to be simplified,
But the rates were high, and she was not shy,
And they say it was only the horse that shied.

When Bloody Mary was made a Guide,
She told the people that when she died
Topographical notes on her views and her votes
If they took her to bits would be found inside.

When Queen Victoria was made a Guide,
She never excelled on the giant stride,
Or won a place in the obstacle race,
And historians doubt if she even tried.

When Messalina was made a Guide . . .
. . . But the trouble is that the form I've tried,
Though far from clever, might last for ever,
With hundreds and hundreds of names beside.

—From The Coloured Lands.

ART CLASS

MARGARETA BERGER-HAMERSCHLAG

My class population consisted of boys and girls between fourteen and twenty years of age. There were thin, undernourished young creatures, stronger ones in spivvish attire with mischief glittering in their eyes, their hair towering in quiffs over stubborn foreheads, languid girls whose faces were covered with an orange plus rose make-up, their hair flowing in curly yellow or brown masses to their shoulders, big lads with an athlete's air. Decently dressed, quiet boys and girls were sprinkled amongst the others. Of the latter a few came forward, telling me about their special interest in painting. One of them was a grammar schoolboy, another a glassblower's apprentice; there were two chemist's trainees, a stone-mason and an electrician. There was also a schoolgirl who said she was very interested "but couldn't draw for tuppence." The boys as well as the girl mentioned that they had come for no other club activities but the art class. . . .

To get an idea of the pupils' backgrounds and interests I sit down next to them and ask them questions while they push their drawing or painting in front of me for criticism. It surprised me to hear that hardly one of them had been to a museum, at least not of their own accord. Most of the boys and girls had never been out of their own district. They couldn't tell me where St. Paul's was nor the Albert Hall. They hadn't been to Piccadilly or even ventured as far out as Kensington. It seems a sort of agoraphobia which keeps them huddling together in their own stable, their own district, though all of them look out longingly towards the fairyland Hollywood. The cinema brings near to them a world entirely different from their own. Where a hundred years ago a slum child knew wealth and splendour only from the glimpse of a carriage passing by, the children of to-day have an inside picture of luxury from films—silver and crystal glittering by candle-light, a richly laid table, nostalgic beaches peopled by carefree young people, furs and cars and beautiful dresses. The cinema has become the shadow of the true life which they wish to lead and which they know pretty well is an out-of-reach dreamland. Their existence is thus cut in two: by day they lead the dreary life of a machinist or an office boy, with chips eaten out of a paper bag, the cracked tea-cup—and by night they identify themselves with glory and wealth at the pictures. What do they care for Piccadilly and the National Gallery? Neither can substitute for their own life one which is realistically, dramatically, different from it, in the way the cinema can.

It was with something of wonder, then, that I listened when that ragged new boy told me that he sometimes went to an art gallery. He liked one picture especially, the *Wandering Jew* by Rembrandt. It fascinated him, he didn't know why. "It's not worth painting," he said, "if one can't paint like that."

His name is Ray, his age over fifteen. He is a beautiful boy with a pink-and-white complexion, almost girlish, but he is strongly built with big, clumsy hands. He works as a carpenter's apprentice on a building site. Ray is tall for his age. He has blue eyes (the first time I have seen forget-me-not blue eyes) under heavy pink lids and a mop of straw-coloured hair. His shirt and jacket are torn but his face and hands are spotlessly clean.

"I don't really know what I want in this class. I'm sure I'm no good at it, but I would like to enlarge that," he said, searching his pocket with one hand and pulling out a very dirty, very torn, tiny photograph of a baby dressed in a woollen romper suit and knitted booties. It looked out of the snapshot with sleepy eyes and a faint little smile.

"That's you, Ray, isn't it?" I asked.

The boy, looking down on his paper, blushed and nodded. There was something queer and moving about his embarrassment so I left him to what he wanted to do.

It nearly took my breath away when I returned to him and saw his drawing. It was virile and brave with that visionary intelligence which is even rare in genuine artists. While I stood there, unable to utter a word, he got up wearily, threw down the crayon like somebody dissatisfied with himself, lifted his arms, stretched himself and murmured: "I can't do it. I thought I wouldn't be able to do it."

I pinned the paper to the blackboard and showed him his own work from a distance. He could see how impressed I was with it and he stood there for a while gazing at it. His sleepy eyes had changed their expression; he looked at it critically and seriously. Then an astonished smile appeared on his thick, childish, rosy lips. He stretched his arms again and in a low voice said: "It's good! It really is good and I thought it was all wrong. Isn't it funny?"

Two evenings later I took all my treasures with me for Ray: the Conté crayons, the umber indian ink, my quills, but Ray didn't come. So I let

196

some of the others use the material and there were some good drawings done. Jean, the girl with the henna-red curls, posed for the class after a promise that she would get two cigarettes for it. But I was rather sad all the evening and tried hard to imagine myself to be Ray. There was something so pathetically resigned in that boy, so hopeless, as if all his life was already behind him and he was content to linger on only because there was no other possibility. I imagined myself outside the club, in the dark street, walking up and down aimlessly, being drawn to the light and the desk, the paper and charcoal, the intensity of doing, and then shrinking back from it and turning into the dark again. I was Ray, hoping and disbelieving at the same time. I felt his smile form on my lips; it made me quite sick to feel it from inside myself. It was such an old smile, the resignation of old age which knows that everything is over. . . .

The classes were rather empty last evening, but quite a number of bored-looking youngsters strolled through the halls and corridor. Only the table tennis room was crowded.

When I signed off in the staff time-book in Jimmy's office he got a telephone call from a club not far from ours, with the warning to look out; a large gang of about thirty boys had smashed up a few things at their place. They had succeeded in getting them out, but the boys had boasted they would smash up another one, which would probably be ours. While Jimmy hung up the receiver, the schoolkeeper rushed in, reporting a crowd of boys in the school yard who looked as if they meant trouble. Jimmy left the man to stand by the telephone to be ready to call the police if it should be necessary, while he and two instructors—the tough ones who teach wrestling and boxing—went out into the yard. I slipped out behind them.

It was an unreal scene, tense, full of foreboding, rather theatrical. The boys stood there in one dark mass, or rather they advanced slowly towards us in the dark, only lighted by the tiny lamp which is fastened over the bicycle shed. None of them spoke, but they all had an expression of gloom and restrained fierceness. I recognized one boy who had been to my class once or twice. I cursed my inability to remember the names of people I don't see regularly but I approached him, though the boxing instructor tried to hold me back by the sleeve. "Hullo," I said to him, touching his arm. "Why don't I see you in my class any longer?"

He shook me off silently; he was like a person in a trance.

Jimmy, with artificial cheerfulness, told them to go home, didn't they know that we closed down at nine-thirty?

"We don't care a b . . . damn if you do, we want to get in!" a tall youth in a long, dark coat with upturned collar growled out.

"We don't care for your b . . . permission, in we go!" shouted another one.

They pressed towards the door while Jimmy and the two men were squeezed into their midst, trying to free themselves and at the same time persuading the boys to be reasonable. There was still dancing and music going on inside, but some of the boys had come out from the hall and stood, hands in their pockets, as onlookers farther back.

I ran into the office and signalled to the schoolkeeper to phone. The first of the gang had reached the corridor, lifted some chairs and banged them against the wall. A few cups from the canteen stood on a tray, ready to be carried into the kitchen for washing. They were dashed to smithereens in a twinkling, also the glass windows of the office door. "Get out of my way or you've had it!" one of the smashers warned me, while his breath came heavily. They worked hard and conscientiously as if they were paid overtime for it and the work had to be finished to schedule. It was a strange sight. Nobody seemed really hysterical, yet it was the same madness which changes peace-loving citizens into warriors or revolutionaries when they are properly worked up. Possibly men need these irrational uproars of antediluvial character. Heaven knows! "That blessed civilization of ours is too much for them," thought I, while I was pushed about in that chaos, deafened by shouts and screams.

At last the police appeared. The boys fled, leaving a jacket here and a muffler there on the ground. Two of the boys were caught, though, but swore to their complete innocence. They had only followed the others, not knowing what it was all about, and they pretended to be highly surprised by the outcome of that excursion.

Glass splinters, torn paper and legs of chairs were lying about and the boxing instructor's face was scratched. A thunderstorm had broken and the culprits were by now probably quiet, gentle and satisfied. . . .

Coming back to my work here I realize that it is the icy atmosphere which makes these clubs so different, not the noise, the swearing, the beastliness of some individuals. Kindness, gratefulness, cheer, are choked in the bud. One sees eyes filled with lethargy and contempt, hearts in which the capacity for love has been sealed off, boredom yawning wide, bodies which act as by mechanical means. . . .

Cynicism and hopelessness are generally not attributes of the young, but here they are. When you see them moving in one big herd it's hard to believe that this mass is made up of individuals. There is no way to resurrect them other than by concentrating on one at a time, making a ceaseless effort to uncover the tiniest spark of life. They are in need of better housing, better food, better backgrounds, it's true, but more urgent is a breath of spiritual life. They'll get their better housing and better food if they have the life to fight for it, instead of being paralysed by barren dreams of wealth, bitter dreams of things they can't come by.

Education can't get at them because their minds are in no way ready to receive through the brain. The films about shoe-making won't save them, but kindness and humour will reach them, so will crafts taught in a serious way; the latter will be a means of releasing latent creative faculties. Holidays in a different setting would do a lot to wake them up and a different attitude towards sex-matters would remove fears which keep most of them in a spasmodic state. The cry is really: "Wake up the dead!" not: "Keep them out of mischief!"

I believe in the human being, I love every movement of its hand, every shade and shape of its face and body. Good and bad are only shades in a variety of tints, but the love of life is the love of everything divine and to find the way to it must be the aim.

—From *Journey into a Fog*.

GOLDEN LADS AND GIRLS

WILLIAM SHAKESPEARE

Fear no more the heat o' the sun,
　　Nor the furious winter's rages;
Thou thy worldly task hast done,
　　Home art gone, and ta'en thy wages;
Golden lads and girls all must,
As chimney-sweepers, come to dust.

Fear no more the frown o' the great;
　　Thou art past the tyrant's stroke;
Care no more to clothe and eat;
　　To thee the reed is as the oak:
The sceptre, learning, physic, must
All follow this, and come to dust.

Fear no more the lightning-flash,
　　Nor the all-dreaded thunder-stone;
Fear not slander, censure rash;
　　Thou hast finish'd joy and moan:
All lovers young, all lovers must
Consign to thee, and come to dust.

No exorciser harm thee!
Nor no witchcraft charm thee!
Ghost unlaid forbear thee!
Nothing ill come near thee!
Quiet consummation have;
And renowned be thy grave!

—From *Cymbeline*.

THE TRUTH ABOUT EDUCATION

G. K. CHESTERTON

Of course, the main fact about education is that there is no such thing.
It does not exist, as theology or soldiering exist. Theology is a word like
geology, soldiering is a word like soldering; these sciences may be
healthy or not as hobbies; but they deal with stones and kettles, with
definite things. But education is not a word like geology or kettles.
Education is a word like "transmission" or "inheritance"; it is not an
object, but a method. It must mean the conveying of certain facts,
views, or qualities to the last baby born. They might be the most trivial
facts, or the most preposterous views, or the most offensive qualities;
but if they are handed on from one generation to another they are
education. Education is not a thing like theology; it is not an inferior
or superior thing; it is not a thing in the same category of terms.
Theology and education are to each other as a love-letter to the General Post Office. Mr. Fagin was quite as educational as Dr. Strong; in
practice probably more educational. It is giving something—perhaps
poison. Education is tradition, and tradition (as its name implies) can
be treason.

This first truth is frankly banal; but it is so perpetually ignored in
our political prosing that it must be made plain. A little boy in a little
house, son of a little tradesman, is taught to eat his breakfast, to take
his medicine, to love his country, to say his prayers, and to wear his
Sunday clothes. Obviously Fagin, if he found such a boy, would teach
him to drink gin, to lie, to betray his country, to blaspheme and to
wear false whiskers. But so also Mr. Salt the vegetarian would abolish
the boy's breakfast; Mrs. Eddy would throw away his medicine; Count
Tolstoy would rebuke him for loving his country; Mr. Blatchford would
stop his prayers; and Mr. Edward Carpenter would theoretically de-
nounce Sunday clothes, and perhaps all clothes. I do not defend any
of these advanced views, not even Fagin's. But I do ask what, between

the lot of them, has become of the solid entity called education. It is not (as commonly supposed) that the tradesman teaches education plus Christianity; Mr. Salt, education plus vegetarianism; Fagin, education plus crime. The truth is, that there is nothing in common at all between these teachers, except that they teach. In short, the only thing they share is the one thing they profess to dislike; the general idea of authority. It is quaint that people talk of separating dogma from education. Dogma is actually the only thing that cannot be separated from education. It *is* education. A teacher who is not dogmatic is simply a teacher who is not teaching.

—From *What's Wrong with the World.*

OUR LADY TEACHES HER SON

RONALD KNOX

God became Man, to remake his world; he became a little child, and I suppose he used to play games; I don't think the Sacred Humanity would have been quite human if our Lord had never played games. And the best playmate he had, if so, was his Blessed Mother, such a short distance away from girlhood herself, who was so good at sympathizing, at seeing other people's points of view. At any rate, she was the Wisdom which accompanied him through all those steps of early childhood. Our Lord had, if he cared to use it, all the knowledge which is enjoyed by the blessed Saints in heaven. But, in order to be perfectly Man, he preferred to acquire knowledge by experience and by hearsay, just as you and I do. He went to school in the carpenter's shop; but his education had begun long before that. He had been learning all the time, "increasing in wisdom," the gospel tells us. And the person who taught him that wisdom was his mother—who else should it be? . . .

You have to think of a mother and her little son, who is just learning to talk in words of one syllable. They are looking out, from some point a bit west of Nazareth, at the great mass of Mount Carmel dominating the plain. And the boy asks, "Ma zeh?" (What's that?). And his mother answers, "That's ha-har [the mountain]; say 'Har', Jesus." Or they are a bit east of Nazareth, and suddenly through a gap in the hills they are looking down, across precipitous miles, at the Lake of Galilee where it forms a blue floor at the bottom of the plain. And this time she says, "Ha-yam [the sea]; say 'Yam', Jesus." Or she takes him with her in the cool of the evening when she carries a jug to draw water at the spring outside the town. There is only one spring at Nazareth, and it is still called the Fountain of the Virgin, after her. And this time she says, "Ha-'en [the spring]; say ' 'En', Jesus." So the mind-pictures of the Incarnate were formed; and when he preached, years later, about a city set on a hill, or fishermen casting their nets into the sea, or a spring of water welling up to eternal life, he was utilizing the wisdom he had learned from that wise playmate of his, long ago.

—From *The Gospel in Slow Motion*.

LIMBO

SISTER

MARY ADA

The Ancient Greyness shifted
Suddenly and thinned
Like mist upon the moors
Before a wind.
An old, old prophet lifted
A shining face and said:
"He will be coming soon.
The Son of God is dead;
He died this afternoon."

A murmurous excitement stirred
All souls.
They wondered if they dreamed—
Save one old man who seemed
Not even to have heard.

And Moses standing,
Hushed them all to ask
If any had a welcome song prepared.
If not, would David take the task?
And if they cared
Could not the three young children sing
The Benedicite, the canticle of praise
They made when God kept them from perishing
In the fiery blaze?

A breath of spring surprised them,
Stilling Moses' words.
No one could speak, remembering
The first fresh flowers,

The little singing birds.
Still others thought of fields new ploughed
Or apple trees
All blossom-boughed.
Or some, the way a dried bed fills
With water
Laughing down green hills.
The fisherfolk dreamed of the foam
On bright blue seas.
The one old man who had not stirred
Remembered home.

And there He was
Splendid as the morning sun and fair
As only God is fair.
And they, confused with joy,
Knelt to adore
Seeing that He wore
Five crimson stars
He never had before.

No canticle at all was sung.
None toned a psalm, or raised a greeting song.
A silent man alone
Of all that throng
Found tongue—
Not any other.
Close to His heart
When the embrace was done,
Old Joseph said,
"How is Your Mother,
How is Your Mother, Son?"

—From *The Mary Book*.

MAY I NOW PRESENT

LUCILE HASLEY

One of the nicest features about public speaking, as far as I'm concerned, is the eternal element of surprise. Almost all other forms of human suffering have an element of sameness about them—that is, at a certain pain level you either go into convulsions or die—but this merciful arrangement doesn't apply to the dry-mouthed agony of stage fright. You just *think* you're going to have convulsions or die: a form of wishful thinking that gets a person nowhere. Mother Nature, apparently figuring that death is too good for amateur public speakers, never steps in. She lets you stand there and sweat it out for yourself.

Yet it's really uncanny, when you stop and think about it, just how much punishment the human system can take and still pull through. Standing before a microphone, you can experience everything but the actual death rattle and yet—O eternal element of surprise!—be able to walk off the platform unaided after it's all over. Fifteen minutes later you're even able to partake of a little nourishment—not, mind you,

206

through intravenous feeding but by actually lifting a cup of hot Orange Pekoe to your own lips. Five minutes later, as the hot tea expands your collapsed arteries and your eyes begin to focus more clearly, you're even able to identify the yellowish blur on the tea table. The yellowish blur resolves into jonquils—and what beautiful *beautiful* jonquils they are. Wordsworth's heart may have leapt up as he beheld a host of golden daffodils, a-dancing in the breeze, but it's nothing to the leap that your heart takes. In fact, your heart would—at this stage of the game—leap at the sight of a bunch of ragweed stuck in a milk bottle. You see, the impact of what you've just gone through has suddenly hit you. The speech is over; you are still alive; the audience didn't even stone you.

As you gaze around with grateful and wonder-drenched eyes, it's remarkable how different everything now looks. The speaker's platform no longer resembles a scaffold, complete with trap door. The size of the auditorium, formerly approximating St. Patrick's Cathedral, seems to have dwindled considerably. The lady who introduced you, now that you look at her more closely, doesn't *actually* look like one of Stalin's henchmen. Maybe she's even someone's mother. And, how utterly fascinating is the lady on your left as she gives you a detailed account of her last summer's trip to Rome. How you tremble with delight as she plunges into her handbag and hauls out a snapshot of St. Peter's basilica, taken on a cloudy day and from a distance of about 500 yards, and explains the small black dots in the lower left-hand corner. The small black dots, it turns out, are some fellow pilgrims who—would you believe it?—were from her old home town of Davenport, Iowa. Harry, the biggest black dot, is now going to dental college and his sister Ruth, the black dot to his left, once had a poem published in the local paper and plans to . . .

(I wonder, did Lazarus—during those first awesome moments when he realized he was back in the land of the living—experience the same joyful appreciation of his fellow men? Exclaim over a yellow jonquil? A cloudy snapshot?)

This painful method of recapturing a lost zest for living—and I heartily recommend it for all those who can't afford a trip to Sun Valley—is based, of course, on a very old principle. Joy through suffering. For instance, there's nothing like being trapped in an old mine shaft for 48 hours to make you discover a new and giddy pleasure in just breathing fresh air again. Or just *breathing*, for that matter.

This, as I say, is the nice feature about public speaking. I can't think of any other unless it's the fact that this joy-through-suffering is not limited to my own selfish self. The audience, upon realizing that I'm through talking and they're now free to go home, also experiences—although in a more passive degree—this same *joie de vivre*.

In this respect, not all public speakers contribute as much as I to the common weal. Other speakers are satisfied with shallow performances that merely delight, edify, inspire, and regale their audiences. After discounting their brilliance, wit, wisdom, larynx control, timing, stage presence, and a few other odd details—well, what have you got left? The audience loves the speaker, the speaker loves his audience, and the whole thing is pretty fruitless. No redemptive suffering, no sense of release, no nothing.

Even so, it would be perfectly all right with me if medical science would alleviate some of this redemptive suffering. Whatever strides medical science may have made in recent years, you're not going to catch *me* genuflecting before the Men in White until they come up with a cure for chronic stage fright. You know, Mr. Webster defines stage fright as "nervousness upon appearing before an audience" but Mr. Webster, although generally reliable, is here indulging in the whimsical understatement. Actually, stage fright is an affliction that combines all the worst features of lockjaw, palsy, morning nausea, and creeping paralysis. Perhaps the worst feature, though, is that you can't —like a sick cat—crawl under a back porch and suffer in dignity. You have to do your suffering right out in the open, with lots of people watching you.

Moreover, the earth is strewn with these s.f. victims, even though it's impossible to present actual statistics. Soul scars are not always apparent to the naked eye. Perhaps the only infallible way to check up on a suspect—a stage fright carrier, so to speak—would be to sneak up behind him and suddenly yell: "It gives me great pleasure to introduce to you this evening. . . ."

This dirty trick, however, would be on a par with locking little children in old iceboxes and I, as a Christian, cannot recommend it. It could unhinge a sensitive person for life. As a Christian alternative, I suggest you just take my word for it that every third person you meet on the street has suffered or will suffer, before completing his life span, from this dread malady.

(Are you the vice-president of some organization? If so, what assurance do you have that the president may not be down with pleurisy at the next meeting? Do you belong to a study group? If so, do you think you can go on forever, just functioning on the telephone committee, and never have to give a paper? Have you been foolhardy enough to write something for publication? If so, don't you realize that people automatically expect writers also to be professional public speakers? Yes, my friends, public speaking can creep up on even those citizens who have led upright and abstemious lives. It isn't necessarily a matter of just falling in with bad companions.)

Yet what, may I ask, are the Men in White doing about all this? Are there any research foundations? No. Has any case of stage fright, no matter how lurid, ever made the medical journals? No. Why, those Men in White haven't even bothered to cook up a Latin term for stage fright and this, to me, is the last indignity. For instance, I happen to know for a fact that a bright pink rash—common to babies and lasting only twenty-four hours—goes under the imposing title of *Roseola Infantum*. Would it be too much to ask, therefore, that stage fright be dignified with the title of *Roseola Adultorum?* Heaven knows that I can break into rosy hives just *thinking* about a forthcoming speech.

Yet not all victims react the same way. Some people, upon facing an audience, turn ashy white—others a chartreuse—and still others a sort of battleship grey. Despite the variance in color scheme, though, they all have one symptom in common. They all shake. So, on second thought, I suppose a more comprehensive title would be *Shakeola*

H

Adultorum?

This may seem like a minor point, this insisting upon an official Latin term, but it just might be a stepping stone to medical recognition. It might even pave the way to the happy day when you can step into a Walgreen drug store and procure the proper medication, either in liquid or capsule form, for *Shakeola Adultorum*. (I, personally, lean toward capsules that could be neatly stashed in one's vest pocket for emergency use . . . sort of like the way diabetics carry around a lump of sugar.)

As it stands,   Walgreen clerk—if asked for a remedy for just plain old stage fright‑ would probably just snicker and slide a 25¢ copy of *Be Glad You're Neurotic* across the counter. Or, worse, one of those Dale Carnegie books on how to magnetize your audience. The thing that's wrong with Dale is that he presupposes everyone *wants* to magnetize an audience. He'd be pretty disgusted, I daresay, with the scope of my ambition; namely, to be able to face an audience without having my stomach turn upside down. Whether or no the audience gets magnetized is their look-out. I'm just interested in my stomach, and this strikes me as a case for the Men in White rather than the Personality Boys.

I may, of course, be taking the wrong approach. Maybe the trouble *is* with my personality, rather than my Mexican-bean stomach, but psychiatric fees being what they are—well, I just thought it'd be cheaper the Walgreen way. I'd certainly feel pretty silly, paying a fat fee to rent a couch, if all I needed—before facing a microphone—was, say, some ground sassafras root and perhaps a wee dash of marijuana. (This is only a wild guess on my part, not being skilled in the lore of herbs and weeds, but—anything, anything, to spur on those Men in White.)

In the long interim, I suppose the only thing to do is string along with our present primitive methods of seeking relief. None of these works, incidentally, but I think they're rather interesting.

For instance, I have been told by a certain well-known and successful speaker—who, lucky dog, claims that *he* is always "sunk in lethargy" as he faces an audience—that I should count up to ten, slowly and silently, before opening my mouth. This silent counting is presumably to intimidate the audience, as it breathlessly waits for the first pearl to drop from your lips, and also give you time to recover your equilibrium. The only drawback to this method, admits my sunk-in-lethargy friend, is that in one known instance the speaker was so frightened that she couldn't remember what numbers *came* between one and ten. This so heightened her inferiority complex that her last estate was worse than her first: a possibility that *I* wouldn't dare take a chance on.

Another lady speaker whom I know follows the Gayelord Hauser method of relaxation. Just before a speech, she lies down for a half hour on an old ironing board, with her feet elevated fourteen inches higher than her head, and lets the blood rush to her brain. Why this should be beneficial, I am not prepared to state. All I know is that *I* don't need an ironing board because the blood rushes to my head the minute I hear: "And so, this evening, it gives me great pleasure . . ."

Moreover, I have never noted any particular therapeutic value in an incipient brain haemorrhage. Maybe it only works for those hardy souls who also follow the Hauser diet of Yogurt, Brewer's yeast, wheat germ, and blackstrap molasses? It stands to reason, I suppose, that anyone who can stomach all *that* isn't likely to get queasy over a mere audience. Yet the price, I feel, is too stiff. I think, if you don't mind, I'll just hold out for those Walgreen capsules. (And certainly the great Caruso, who said "Each time I sing I feel there is someone waiting to destroy me," is of no help to me. He, to relieve nervous tension while waiting in the wings, would gargle with salt water, inhale Swedish snuff, down a glass of whiskey, chase it with seltzer, and eat a quarter of an apple.)

Several months ago, though, I ran across a method that struck me as having real possibilities. I happened to catch a vaudeville show in Chicago, starring this comedian called Henny Youngman, and it opened up wide vistas. This Henny Youngman character walks out on the stage with a violin, see, but never gets around to playing it. All he

does is just *talk.*

Right away, I realized that here was another stage fright victim—only a very clever one. That violin, clutched in his hot little hand, was merely a symbol of safety to him—a shield of good purpose—and it also served to distract his audience. Expecting to hear the sweet strains of "Humoresque" at any given moment, the audience was too keyed up to notice his quivering Adam's apple or whether his talking made any sense. All eyes were on the violin.

After I get my own violin, for I daresay this Youngman doesn't have a patent on the idea, I fully expect public speaking to become a breeze. I am even, matter of fact, thinking of going Youngman one better. What's wrong with getting myself a nice big bass viol, eh? I could then sit down behind it, completely hidden from view, and read my notes in comfort. Maybe even have a cigarette or munch some Karmel Korn while I was about it. All the audience would be able to see would be my right arm, coming around the bass viol, with my fingers lightly and tantalizingly resting on the strings. As they waited for the first rich deep "pling" (which never comes) to come forth, I would take advantage of their distraction and get the speech out of the way.

Too, this "come out, come out, wherever you are" arrangement would spare me from those feminine speculations that now reach me, as if by mental telepathy, across the footlights: "Wonder why she ever selected *that* hat?"—"Do you suppose she knows what that shade of green does to her?"—"She looks lots older than her photograph, doesn't she?"—"I'll bet she'd die if she knew her underskirt was showing . . ."

Safe and cozy behind my bass viol, they wouldn't even know if my stocking seams were straight or not.

All in all, I think it's going to be nothing short of sensational (easily topping Evelyn and her magic violin that she—with no sense of showmanship—actually *plays*) and there's only one thing that bothers me. That is, I'm going to have to keep my figure chiseled down so as to *fit* behind a bass viol. I just may be forced to take up yogurt and blackstrap molasses after all.

—From *The Mousehunter.*

ON EUPHEMISM

HILAIRE BELLOC

The Euphemism is a little creature deserving the closest attention. Its origin is always of interest, its youth and early growth of still greater interest, its struggle to maturity absorbing. Even when it has worn smooth in age and become a commonplace it is still a much better subject of study than the contemporaries of its youth might imagine. The Euphemism as a species is probably as old as human speech: and how old that is nobody knows, least of all the philologists. The Euphemism is born of that social sense without which man would not be man, and because it is so true a child of that sense it reflects from every facet characters of *Homo Civis,* Man the Citizen.

The Euphemism is a recognition by man of man's own imperfection, and at the same time a recognition by man that he belongs to better things. It is play acting, but none the worse for that. *It is a false word substituted for the true word in order to soften the shock of reality.*

A man stands on a platform. He is about to address a packed audience of Swindlers, Cowards, Bounders, Painted Harridans and Trulls. He opens his mouth to address them. What does he say? He says: "Ladies and gentlemen." Human language should be packed with Euphemisms. It is, indeed, proof that man was meant to live with his fellows, and proof also of how difficult it is for man to carry on that task without inordinate friction. It testifies also to the ingenuity of man himself, for we must note that the Euphemism ninety-nine times out of a hundred rises up from the masses; it has no one author, or if it has, that author is rarely known.

Take the commonest of the Euphemisms, the use of the second or third person in the place of the first. We say "You" instead of "Thou" because (Heaven knows how long ago!) it was thought more polite to

214

pretend that the person addressed was too grand to be treated as a mere individual. He might not be a monarch, but it was only decent to give him the title of one. It is very pretty to see that in the transition towards the Dark Ages both the second person plural and the third person singular came into use for courteous address, and we keep up the habit to this day for the better conduct of human affairs. We write to an ambassador, "Your Excellency will hardly have failed to observe," where brute nature would have written "Don't sham ignorance." It is all to the good so to soften the edges of life. But, in connection with this useful and honourable human habit, remark that the Euphemism sometimes avenges itself. When it finds it is being overworked it revives with added force an original simple use which it was supposed to supplant. Thus the French express both insult and affection by saying "Thou" instead of "You," and in English we use "Thou" for adoration.

The Euphemism is sometimes killed at birth and often killed in early youth. The wealthy and the powerful are always suspicious of it. A new Euphemism is nearly always Middle Class; usually it has to fight hard to get accepted. I could quote half a dozen which I have seen in my own lifetime either done to death or thrust down into the lower ranks of society to which they have, ever since their fall, been inexorably condemned. The use of "homely" as a Euphemism for ugly is an example in point; others, far more striking, I forbear to record through the respect I owe you.

Among Euphemisms thus ruthlessly exiled from the great world, never to re-enter it, are "mansion" and "approach." Both of them were originally of a very roundabout grandeur. Mansion (which is *mansio*) simply meant the place where you stop, and Approach was just approach; the way by which you got near to a place. But hardly had they taken on the air of grandeur when the wealthier classes came out against them to do battle and thrust them back into obscurity. But in doing so they again transformed them. Mansion became one of fifty ways of saying (in the plural) a town flat, while Approach, after lingering painfully, licking its wounds for half a century, died—round about the seventies or eighties, I think. At any rate, it is well dead now. We know "Drive" or

"Avenue," but "Approach" is forgotten.

"Villa" is another glorious specimen. A "Villa" was a country estate of the Roman rich; a village community with the Lord's Great House in the midst. The word was then borrowed to save the face of the suburbs. Now it has a disdainful sound. You may hear a rich woman say of some habitation she despises: "Oh! no! nothing of that sort! Just a villa."

It is sadly true of the Euphemism that when it has got itself well rooted and established it dies in another way: not by losing its body, but by losing its soul. It becomes a commonplace word like any other. We come to use it straightforwardly, as though it had never been a Euphemism at all. A Judge in Chambers, Chamber music, the Upper Chamber, all the hundred uses of that word, come from the late Latin for a vault. It was thought more polite to allude to a man's room as his "vaults" because the great Roman palaces would be vaulted where the little Roman houses had plain flat floors and roofs. When you talk of the "camber" of the road, you are using the same word but in quite another sense. And, what is amusing, you talk of the camera in photography with no sort of relation to any vault at all, nor even to any house, but a box.

Euphemisms grow unnaturally and dangerously by competition, very much as do advertisements, superlatives, and words of emphasis. One Euphemism will supplant another in a few years and then be destroyed again in its turn, like the outlaw of the Nemi wood by a supplanter. A neat case of this which has happened almost within a lifetime is the Euphemism for madhouse. A madhouse is something unpleasant; so, man being a social animal, he must give it a name pleasanter than the true one. He began early by calling it a Bethlehem, from a charitable foundation dedicated to the Nativity and coming to function as a refuge for the afflicted. Hence Bedlam. When Bedlam had ceased to be even tolerably polite, we invented asylum. Asylum is a very beautiful word. It should by rights be full of repose and peace, for it means a secure refuge. But Asylum wore thin in less than a century. We have got by now to "Mental Hospital"; and it is a sad tribute to the divine intelligence of man that "mental" already means with the poor (and perhaps in time

will mean with the rich) a person of distracted mind. What Euphemism will men use when they have grown frightened of "Mental Hospital"?

We never know what the next Euphemism will be. It comes up out of the depths and steals upon us unawares. I doubt whether a locution which is a favourite with the leisured English will ever take final root, though I confess I am very fond of it myself because it always reminds me of that high genius in whose writings I first found it: P. G. Wodehouse. I mean, the term "loony-bin." It is admirable, it is first-rate, therefore it will go down the dark way which all the best things of this world must tread; the road to oblivion: the unreturning way. Perhaps it will not die in my time, but if it does I shall mourn it sincerely.

And so much for Euphemism. Do not attempt to live without it in a fit of straightforwardness, for if you do you will pass an unhappy manhood and a lonely old age. Not that I care.

—From *The Silence of the Sea.*

EPIGRAM

REV. NATHANIEL WARD (1578–1652)

The world is full of care, much like unto a bubble;
Women and care, and care and women, and women
and care and trouble.

PARIS THEN

J. B. MORTON

So Van Dongen is to have an exhibition in London. Well, well! Van
Dongen, with whom I used to take a *bock* at the *Vache qui Chante*,
while Gornowicz expounded Cubism, and Fracas, the poet, recited his
verses to the waiters. In those days I lived with Vaurien on the floor of a
charcuterie in the *Rue des Saltimbanques,* and when we had *deux
sous,* we used to dine off a *petit pain* sent us by Mère Cauve, from the
boulangerie next door.

Slotz, the Belgian, was one of us, and Siliani, the painter, and La
Saperlipopette, the dancer. What days! What days!

And now Van Dongen is famous and the old *Chèvre qui Murmure*
is an auction room, and nobody goes to the *Mirliton.*

They were good days, and we were really bohemians. "Dong," as I
called him then, and I used to dine often on a *bouteille de vin rouge*
and a *croissant*—he fresh from his easel, I in an interval between two
articles for the *Revue de Jeudi.* Sometimes "Pic" (Picasso) and "Mo"
(Modigliani) would *joindre* us, bringing their own *soupe.*

There was Souris, with his flashing brown eyes and his loud laugh. He mixes now with the world of rank and fashion, but in those days we had but one hat between us—a brimless straw—and when it was raining we used to toss up for who should go and buy the *petit pain* for the night's supper. It was Souris who threw a kipper at a *gendarme* in the *Place Ridicule*. All this was, of course, before his *"Bonsoir Mariette"* was produced at the *Comédie Française*, and brought him fame.

Others who frequented our set in those days were Henri Culotte, Rostand, "Pif," Bourget, Mirabeau, Camille Ducart, France, Matisse, Monet, Manet, Minet, Munet *et* Menet, *vous savez.* What days! *Quels jours!*

In those days Renoir, Jean Coquelin, Rostand, Degas, George Moore, Verlaine, Rodin, Maeterlinck, Rimbaud, Hérédia, de l'Isle Adam, Massenet, Picasso, Bordeaux, Verhaeren, Hugo, Dumas, Gambetta, Bazaine, Rémy de Gourmont, Loti, de Chavannes, Watteau, Rousseau, Gautier, Boulanger, Béranger, and I used to share an attic in the *Avenue Boissy d'Anglas,* and I remember "Pic" saying to me that so great was the confusion in that small room that one hardly knew whether one was writing, painting, drinking absinthe, composing music, or modelling a bust.

One evening Picasso fastened an old boot of Moore's to his canvas, painted it green, and called it "The Lost Promontory." And that was the birth of Blaguism, which was to sweep the art-world of two capitals. After that we had butter with our rolls, and Verlaine stopped wearing Rodin's tie as a belt.

How gay the cabarets were in those days. I shall never forget as long as I live one night when La Praline was dancing at the *Moulin du Gâteau.* Verlaine kept on throwing parsley at her, until she jumped down from the table and pulled his hair. How Rodin laughed. "Aha" he said, *"Le rire est sur toi, Paul. Ça, c'était un à lui, mon ami."* And Verlaine joined in the general laugh, until Gounod pushed him off his chair.

Fracas and I had written an epic, but it came to nothing, and we eked out a living by drawing on the walls of the local restaurant until

220

Victor Hugo read some of our verse, and asked to meet us. Along we went to a small restaurant near the *Abattoir*, and the master introduced us to Daudet, Loti, Karr, de Goncourt, Gautier, Lamartine and Pascal, all of whom complimented us. Alas, we were destined never to meet any of them again.

After the publication of my serial in the *Journal des Débats* Fracas and I moved to a better attic, in the *Rue Daunou*, where our roommates included de Maupassant, Zola, Dreyfus, Baudelaire, Debussy, Van Gogh, Jaurès, Anatole France and Israel de la Tour. It was here that I first met Sarah Bernhardt, and I still treasure a boot on which she signed her autograph for me—there was nothing else in the room to write on, for we were poor in those days, and Zola and I had just pawned Baudelaire's life-size model of an albatross.

Dear Zola, I wonder where he is now. I wonder.

Baudelaire was then a student at the *Ecole Normale et Supérieure des Sciences Inutiles et des Mauvais Arts,* and he used to say that he would one day write an epic of Hell on the sky in letters of sulphurous fire. But we knew he was only joking.

One day while I was drinking a *bock chez* Prunier, who should sit down at my table but my old friend Toulouse Lautrec. He asked me to start a paper with him, so I did. We wrote it all ourselves, and Toulouse designed decorations. It was called the *Cri de Montmartre,* and we had France, Bernstein, Bergson and Solenberg writing for us. We attacked everything, and the paper caused quite a stir in the *Rue des Odeurs Incroyables,* where Verlaine, Franck, Gide, Maurras, Daudet, Gambetta and I were living in an attic at the time. After three weeks we had to cease publication, as we could not afford to pay any bills. But it was in this paper that there first appeared the verses of Paul Fort, known as the Prince of Poets. He held his court in those days at the *Closerie des Lilas,* and there "Bim" used to draw ostriches on the pavement far on into the small hours.

—From *By the Way.*

PARIS NOW

J. B. MORTON

Café des Vaches,
Paris

I am basking in the Parisian sunlight, drinking my Pernod and watching the cosmopolitan crowd passing up and down the boulevard.

From my table I can see old *père* Nichaud, the doyen of the Poupouists, and a disciple of Apollinaris, who taught me how to draw mackerel with my eyes shut.

Ah, Lolotte has just entered. Lolotte, the little dancer from the *Brebis Qui Tousse,* who used to shoot plums off the trees with a rook-rifle—how long ago?

With her is handsome young Fujiyama, the Japanese artist, and Dolmen, the dour Cornish poet who strangled La Folie with his braces at the corner of the *Rue des Mauvaises Odeurs.*

"*Garçon!*"

Surely I know that *voix.*

Assurément! It is "Gop," the wicked caricaturist of the *Calviniste du Nord,* the go-ahead paper that first printed Dubosc's explanation of Proust.

We greet each other.

"*Tiens, mon vieux!*"

"*Et vous?*"

"*Pas mal.*"

"Gop" married the widow Colifichet, because he owed her four months' rent. He and Puant are the authors of "*Bonsoir, Nou-Nou!*" the new revue at the Alouette.

He was a wild young man in his youth, this "Gop," and used to drop eggs from the top of the Eiffel Tower.

223

At a corner table, in the shade, Manon, from the *Grands Augustins,* is talking to Mathilde Mercredi, the *soubrette* from the *Samaritaine.* "Tic" greets them. He is smoking one of his long Cuban cigars at the wrong end, and his trousers are patched with leading articles from the *Ami du Peuple.*

"*Hé, Manon!*"

The slim girl starts, and looks up.

"*Mais . . . tais-toi!*"

Here comes Tric-Trac, who sells his own songs at ten sous the kilo every evening in the Place Pigalle. They say he has written an opera in which he makes use of only three notes.

Ah, now for a real Bohemian—Paradis, in his velvet coat and black trousers, with his pale, dirty face and eyes that burn like live coals. He is dying, they say. He sleeps in the day-time, and drinks all night, but if he cared he could be a great artist.

Paradis was brought up on his father's estate in the Morvan, but he ran away to a publisher's (the modern equivalent of running away to sea) and managed to get a novel published. It failed, and he did no more work.

His father makes him a handsome allowance, and he lives in the *Rue Chat Maigre* with Tortoise, the poet, and Beaugras, the etcher.

At a table on the pavement I note Van Kuypers, the Dutchman. With him is La Grenouille, who sits for Garnache. When he becomes excited he pours his coffee into his coat-pocket and takes off his boots. They say that he has a crayon frieze running round the lining of his hat, representing a boar-hunt in the forest of Quercy.

La Grenouille sleeps in a canoe which is anchored to the side of a big swimming bath, but she keeps a mole in a fur glove suspended from the ceiling.

The sun sinks. The café teems with life.

Ah, Paris!

A clock in the Rue Manet strikes six-thirty, and I think of those words of de Gourmont.

—From *Morton's Folly.*

224

TOUJOURS LA POLITESSE

There was a young man called MacSweeny
Who drank seven quarts of Martini;
And the Paris police
Sent a wire to his niece:
"Nous regrettons MacSweeny est fini."

OF THE DANGERS
ATTENDING ALTRUISM ON
THE HIGH SEAS

G. K. CHESTERTON

Observe these Pirates bold and gay,
   that sail a gory sea:
notice their bright expression:—
   the handsome one is me.

We plundered ships and harbours,
    we spoiled the Spanish main;
but Nemesis watched over us,
    for it began to rain.

Oh all well-meaning folk take heed!
    Our Captain's fate was sore;
a more well-meaning Pirate
    had never dripped with gore.

The rain was pouring long and loud,
    the sea was drear and dim;

a little fish was floating there:
    our Captain pitied him.

"How sad," he said, and dropped a tear,
    splash on the cabin roof,
"that we are dry, while he is there
    without a waterproof.

"We'll get him up on board at once;
    for Science teaches me,
he will be wet if he remains
    much longer in the sea."

They fished him out; the First Mate wept,
    and came with rugs and ale:
the Boatswain brought him one golosh,
    and fixed it on his tail.

But yet he never loved the ship;
  against the mast he'd lean:
if spoken to, he coughed and smiled,
  and blushed a pallid green.

Though plied with hardbake, beef and beer,
  he showed no wish to sup:
the neatest riddles they could ask,
  he always gave them up.

They seized him and court-martialled him,
 in some excess of spleen,
for lack of social sympathy,
 (Victoria XII. 18).

They gathered every evidence
 that might remove a doubt:
they wrote a postcard in his name,
 and partly scratched it out.

Till, when his guilt was clear as day,
    with all formality,
they doomed the traitor to be drowned,
    and threw him in the sea.

The flashing sunset, as he sank,
    made every scale a gem;
and, turning with a graceful bow,
    he kissed his fin to them.

MORAL

I am, I think I have remarked,
  terrifically old
(the second Ice-age was a farce,
  the first was rather cold).

A friend of mine, a Trilobite,
  had gathered in his youth,
when Trilobites *were* Trilobites,
  this all-important truth.

We aged ones play solemn parts—
  sire—guardian—uncle—king.
Affection is the salt of life,
  kindness a noble thing.

The old alone may comprehend
  a sense in my decree;
but—if you find a fish on land,
  oh throw it in the sea.

—From *Greybeards at Play*.

The drawings are those of G. K. Chesterton.

CHINESE SONG

J. B. MORTON

Yoo-Hoo went down to the pagoda,
Carrying a heap of bamboo.
He got bitten by a horse
Of the Ming dynasty.
(Sho-pi: circa 1236 B.C.)

—From *The Misadventures of Dr. Strabismus.*

NEUROTICS AND SAINTS

CARYLL HOUSELANDER

It is—one cannot repeat too often—possible for a neurotic to be a saint, and possible that a neurosis or a mental illness, as much as any other illness, may be the means by which someone may sanctify himself. On the other hand, sanctity and neurosis are not the same thing. No one ever became a saint *because* he was neurotic, though anyone could become a saint through the truly heroic means of sanctifying his neurosis. The difficulty here, which puzzles the outside observer, is that whilst sanctity and neurosis in themselves are two different things, the outward symptoms of both are often alike.

232

Nevertheless it is not surprising that many people confuse sanctity with neurosis, for superficially, and even to a certain extent on deeper levels, saints and neurotics have much in common, much that makes it difficult to distinguish one from the other with certainty. There is a reason for this that goes deeper than the obvious one, which is that in spite of the fact that every individual is uniquely himself, there are certain basic factors which all human beings have in common simply because they are human beings.

To begin with the most superficial thing of all, and yet an exterior thing which expresses what is hidden in a man: appearance and dress. There are saints in every grade of society, from kings and courtiers to beggars and monks, and therefore saints who are dressed in scarlet or in rags, or even in black coats and tweeds. But it is the ragged sanctity which stands out in the imagination of those who know the saints only from a distance, and therefore know only those who are outwardly most conspicuous.

Now put Benedict Joseph Labre, who is a saint, by the side of Arthur Rimbaud, who is a degenerate; they are both in rags, they are both unwashed, it might be very difficult to know at a glance which was the saint and which the sinner. More so because both are consciously in revolt against society, and choose their rags.

Or compare the depressing description of St. Gemma Galgani, in her dowdy black dress and hat, which made her a joke to the Italian street urchins, with one of those morbidly shy women who dress in just such a way because they secretly dare not put their charm to the test.

We cannot spot our saint by his clothes, but neither is it always easy to know him by his way of thought, or by what he does or says. There are many things commonly done both by neurotics and saints, things which we would regard as hysteria, or even vice, and certainly would be unwilling to tolerate in members of our own family, and in this we should seldom differ from the saints' own relations in their time. There is, for example, flagellation, self-starvation, vagabondage. It is true that the average hagiographer would give different names to these peculiarities, but those are the terms that might well be used if it were not pre-

233

supposed that we were speaking of saints.

It is not always easy to distinguish between the ways of thought of saints and lunatics. I have myself been given a most edifying explanation by a lunatic of how his life was modelled on that of St. Teresa of Lisieux. In "offering up" (he told me) every detail in life for the glory of God, he sanctified every "indifferent" action. Thus he had on three separate occasions been able to make even so simple and indifferent an act as the swinging of a club holy (on three occasions he had swung it down on old ladies' heads).

DANIEL BOOTER
ROUTE SIX

ALBERT F. GRIFFITH

I seen the same old sights so long
I get all scraped and screwed-up like inside
Each time I look.
I'm tired, real tired of blotting out the sight
Each night before I sleep.

They say the country's fine: you think
They ever see the other half—the half
That's made of dirty chicken roosts
That smell and teem with maggots when they're wet?
And cows with teats they cut while break-
Ing through the cob-wire fence to eat
Your watermelon vines and squash?

(The teats, they pus and scab and so the cows
They kick and get manure in the milk.)
Tomaters fester sud-gray blisters in the sun
And rot and stink like canteloupes—
I never seen a 'mater crop out here do good:
The best you get's enough to eat, and them
Ain't worth the while to pick 'em.
I just take a pinch of salt and carry it
With me in the fields,
And stop and pick me one or two—all hot
And sunny-tasting from the vine;
You can't beat that for taste: ain't nothin' like
The limp and sad and unripe fruit you buy
In city stores:
They just taste salted, hard,
And kind of fresh like earth in just-plowed furrows.
They're good; the kind of thing that sort of
Makes you want to stay.

SCHOOL: ENGLISH COMPOSITION

G. K. CHESTERTON

Exercise CCXXII. B: *The "Tomato" in Prose and Prosody*

No subject has so deeply agitated modern life, or presented so profound
a problem to the modern conscience, as the matter of the different
pronunciations of the word "tomato," and all lesser matters of morals,
manners, religion and civilization may well be set aside, and their
barren quarrels suspended, while this vital matter is decided in the
serious manner it demands.

Already a divergence of pronunciation on this point has divided
the two great Anglo-Saxon communities, on whose friendship depends
the peace of the world, our American cousins preferring, for reasons
best known to themselves, to pronounce "tomato" as if it were meant
to rhyme to "potato." Thus, in the little known companion poem to
"The Village Blacksmith" entitled "The Village Greengrocer," the poet
Longfellow observes with a simplicity that is his alone

> If you meet the Village Maiden
> Pause: and give her a tomato:
> Or if shyly she refuse it
> Offer her a large potato.

But this pronunciation was no provincialism of the rustic and the innocent. In the famous passage in "The Raven," Edgar Allan Poe himself writes:

> With a heart as cold as Cato's, or the pallid bust of Plato's
> That I keep with canned tomatoes just above my chamber
> > door.

On the other hand the typical outburst of Walt Whitman concerning
"Tomatoes; tomatoes everywhere, raw, red, utterly uneatable: me

236

myself also as raw and red as any tomato," does not, with all its quiet beauty, throw any light on the elocutionary question.

But a graver question has arisen touching the accentuation of the word. Even our Anglo-Saxon cousins apparently manage to agree with us in accenting the penultimate syllable. There has, however, appeared in the West Country a poetical group, a nest of singing-birds, described by hostile critics as a nest of Roman Catholics,* who openly accent the first syllable to the word, turning it into a dactyl, and producing a sound resembling that of "tommy-toes."

Authorities are not easy to adduce. Shakespeare has only one doubtful reference to tomatoes, on which the commentators differ: Duffins reading "comatose" and Boxsheim "come at once." Milton's description of the light lunch given by Eve to Adam,

Tomatoes tolerant and cucumber mild,

is not, to anyone familiar with Miltonic variations, final touching his view of tomatoes, though decisive enough of his very Miltonic emphasis on cucumbers. The eighteenth century is almost silent. The tomato is too wild and fantastic an object to grow in the trim rose-garden of Pope or even of Cowper. Burns indeed has the line:

Wisht grumly claucht tomato tizzy

but it is not easy to infer the sound of one word in a line, while we cannot reproduce the sound of any of the others.

There follows a gap: Byron, with his hasty arrogance, ignored the tomato: its presence escaped the drugged abstraction of Coleridge. Curiously enough, a tomato is almost the only object in the universe to which Shelley does not compare the Cloud or the Skylark. And it adds a darker shade to the tragedy of the early death of Keats to reflect that, had he lived and his powers expanded, he would doubtless have given his best work to the rich and glowing topic of tomatoes. With the Victorians the tomato reappears—like the pomegranate. Tenny-

* Cf. The essay in *The Thing* called "Who Are the Conspirators?"

son's stress is as usual traditional,

> The riped tomato grows from green to red
> As grows from green to red the dusk of day.

But Swinburne is for the revolutionary prosody,

> When red were the apples of Venus
> And bitter with poisonous mirth
> When tomatoes panted between us,
> Red tomatoes bursting at birth.

Mr. W. B. Yeats appears to follow his first masters, the Pre-Raphaelite poets, in this as in some other things: but his later poetic licence leaves the point doubtful:

> I went into Kidnoggin Wood
> With a dried laughter in my mind:
> I tore seven tomatoes with my teeth
> For laughter never can be kind.

Here it seems probable that the new dactylic scansion is employed. The rather irregular verse of Miss Edith Sitwell,

> The sky bulges through the skylight like a blue tomato,

throws no light on what accent she gives to the word, or indeed on what meaning she attaches to it.

   NOTE. There is a poem by Browning, which the Browning Society believes to be about a tomato: but as the word is not used and the poem is entitled "Ben-Hafiz Self-Examines," the question of pronunciation does not arise.

—From *Return to Chesterton.*

238

JABBERWOCKY REVISITED

JOHN CHARLOT[*]

Although Lewis Carroll's poetry was not understood in his day, it is greatly appreciated at present. Though most people recognize his genius, there are still, at present, some itinerant individuals who prosaically protest that they do not understand it and that neither does anyone else. It is for these scattered remnants of bourgeoisie that I write this article.

Notice that I have purposely chosen one of Carroll's more obscure poems so that I will not be hampered by individual interpretation from all sides.

JABBERWOCKY

'Twas brillig, and the slithy toves
Did gyre and gimble in the wabe;
All mimsy were the borogoves,
And the mome raths outgrabe.

"Beware the Jabberwock, my son!
The jaws that bite, the claws that catch!
Beware the Jubjub bird, and shun
The frumious Bandersnatch!"

[*] A pupil at Portsmouth Priory School.

He took his vorpal sword in hand;
Long time the manxome foe he sought—
So rested he by the Tumtum tree,
And stood awhile in thought.

And as in uffish thought he stood,
The Jabberwock, with eyes of flame,
Came whiffling through the tulgey wood,
And burbled as it came!

One, two! One, two! And through and through
The vorpal blade went snicker-snack!
He left it dead, and with its head
He went galumphing back.

"And hast thou slain the Jabberwock?
Come to my arms, my beamish boy!
O frabjous day! Callooh, Callay!"
He chortled in his joy.

'Twas brillig, and the slithy toves
Did gyre and gimble in the wabe;
All mimsy were the borogoves,
And the mome raths outgrabe.

If you still persist in denying the readability of this great poem, read
on and I shall explain its obvious and subtle nuances.

"Twas brillig." For this interpretation I turn directly to Lewis Carroll's tone poem "Alice Through the Looking-Glass" in which he says
that brillig is the time when people usually broil things. Thus the late
afternoon. How he arrives at this conclusion heaven only knows.

"And the slithy toves." You know Dr. and Mrs. Maurice Tove, the
neighbors of Lewis Carroll, whom he heartily disliked.

"Did Gyre and Gimble in the Wabe." Gyre and Gimble's was the

Macy's of his day and obviously the good people were shopping at the Imported Chinese Wabe Dept.

"*All mimsy were the borogroves.*" The borogroves are naught but the public parks (the borough groves). That Carroll thought of them as mimsy, only goes to point up his understanding of nature and his puckish personality.

"*And the mome raths outgrabe.*" Again I am forced to turn to "Alice Through the Looking-Glass" I found the passage in which he states that raths are little pigs that are lost from mome, and an outgrabe is a cross between a squeal and a grunt. Thus the pigs are returning to the barn after a hard day at the pasture.

"*Beware the Jabberwock, my son.*" I think this is the time to let out the secret of the Jabberwocky. The key to deciphering the poem is that the poem is entirely allegorical. The Jabberwock personifies one of the sins or vices to which mankind commonly are prey. After minutes of research on the part of my colleagues and myself, we have come to the conclusion that the vice that is personified is the nasty habit of biting one's nails. Therefore, the vorpal sword mentioned in the opening line of the third verse is nothing but a nail file.

"*Beware the jaws that bite.*" Obvious!

"*The claws that catch.*" Teeth *do* do a very haphazard job.

"*Beware the Jubjub bird.*" The Jubjub bird for reasons I will not trifle to enter into is known to be the ancient Parynosaurus. The father also contrasts his son's habit to the Bandersnatch of frumious fame.

"*Manxome foe.*" Manxome comes partly from the Latin word *manus* meaning hand and from the Egyptian word !!——! which means literally "out on a limb." Thus he seeks his fingernails.

"*Tumtum tree.*" This is the tree from which the Polynesian aborigines make their war drums or Tom-toms. Explorers say that the tom-tom has a peculiar, flat sound.

"*Uffish thought.*" Sad to say, our hero *is* a bit of a snob.

"*The Jabberwock with eyes of flame, came whiffling through the tulgey wood.*" The thought of biting his nails suddenly comes to our hero. Though some people have tried to identify the tulgey wood with the

English mentality, I will leave it to the reader's discretion.

"The vorpal blade went snicker-snack." He conquers the temptation and dexterously cuts his fingernails off with his manicure scissors.

"He left it dead, etc." He has finally broken the habit and runs to show his father the neatly cut fingernails scattered about the grass.

"Come to my arms, my beamish boy." This was doubtless answered "Aw shucks, Paw. 'Tweren't nothin'."

"Callooh, Callay." This is the father's present wife and his daughter by his last marriage.

See! Once one understands a bit more one is able to look at the poem as a whole.

It is sundown. Mother is cooking dinner. The dear Toves, God bless them, are buying some lovely Chinese wabe which is currently the vogue. As the sun goes down, it bathes the park in soft rosy tints and the groves, feeling the delicious warmth around them, frolic as the breeze playfully moves their branches in a slow, soft minuet. The swine return from the mud.

Suddenly we hear a violent quarrel. A father bawls out his son in no uncertain terms. The son has stigmatized his father in the business world by biting his nails all over the dress of some dowager with a thousand pound account. The son goes out under the tumtum tree silently weeping over the fate God has sent him to overcome. Suddenly through his tulgey brain comes the desire, the thirsting craving desire! He must bite his nails! He wrestles with himself madly. He thinks of Emily, of the children and the life he loves. He quickly cuts the fingernails with the manicure scissors provided for such occasions. All at once there is a glorious throbbing in his breast. He has conquered. He has proved himself a man.

I trust that you all see the point of the poem now. Through the wild plot, mad words and racy dialogue Lewis Carroll has managed to bring out a lesson that has thrilled mankind, filled mankind with confidence to overcome future trouble.

BUY JOHNSON AND JOHNSON CUTICLE SCISSORS!

BOB-UP-AND-DOWN

G. K. CHESTERTON

Irresponsible outbreak of one who, having completed a book of enormous length on the Poet Chaucer, feels himself freed from all bonds of intellectual self-respect and proposes to do no work for an indefinite period.

> "Wot ye not wher ther start a litel town,
> Which that icleped is Bob-up-an-down."
> THE CANTERBURY TALES.

They babble on of Babylon,
They tire me out with Tyre,
And Sidon putting side on,
I do not much admire.
But the little town Bob-up-and-Down,
That lies beyond the Blee,
Along the road our fathers rode,
O that's the road for me.

In dome and spire and cupola
It bubbles up and swells
For the company that canter
To the Canterbury Bells.
But when the Land Surveyors come
With maps and books to write,
The little town Bob-up-and-Down
It bobs down out of sight.

I cannot live in Liverpool,
O lead me not to Leeds,
I'm not a Man in Manchester,
Though men be cheap as weeds:
But the little town Bob-up-and-Down,
That bobs towards the sea,
And knew its name when Chaucer came,
O that's the town for me.

I'll go and eat my Christmas meat
In that resurgent town,
And pledge to fame our Father's name
Till the sky bobs up and down;
And join in sport of every sort
That's played beside the Blee,
Bob-Apple in Bob-up-and-Down,
O that's the game for me.

Now Huddersfield is Shuddersfield,
And Hull is nearly Hell,
Where a Daisy would go crazy
Or a Canterbury Bell,
The little town Bob-up-and-Down
Alone is fair and free,
For it can't be found above the ground,
O that's the place for me.

—From *The Coloured Lands*.

A LITTLE PEACH IN THE
ORCHARD GREW

LUCILE HASLEY

All I had to do, said the magazine quiz, was to answer the questions truthfully and spontaneously, add up my score, and turn to page 105. On page 105 would be the grand unveiling: was I the Mother Type or was I the Wife Type?

To me, this seemed to offer a very narrow range of possibilities. What if, under my housewifely exterior, I was really the Harem Type or the Gun Moll Type or the Helen of Troy Type? None of these was very likely but, still, I resented the stuffy limitations set by this Dr. Albert O'Whoosis who had concocted the quiz. Dr. Albert O'Whoosis, not realizing that I had once been hailed as the Peach Type, was underestimating my more lush possibilities.

Back in South Bend Central High School, in the school *Interlude,* they had printed "A little peach in the orchard grew" under my graduation picture and *this,* I would have you know, was a triumph of no mean scope. Lots of the other girls had to be content with noncommittal and lacklustre sentiments like "Who shall find a valiant woman?" or "Prithee! Hark! A maid doth enter" or "Her voice was ever gentle, soft, and low, an excellent thing in woman."

At the age of seventeen, none of us gave a hoot about being soft-spoken or valiant women but "peach" . . . well, now, *there* you had something. Something more on the Clara Bow order. I distinctly remember that none of the more laudable honors that came my way (making the varsity volley-ball team and winning a debate about the Panama Canal) carried the full fruity flavor of my *Interlude* analysis. Even to-day, whenever I open a tin of canned peaches, I always read the label (Grade A . . . hand-picked . . . packed in regulation heavy syrup) with a certain proud nostalgia. Yes, sir!

246

You can readily understand, therefore, why the proposed stakes in this magazine quiz hurt my feelings. Why, this upstart of a professor wasn't even giving me a *chance* to see if I had the makings of anything interesting. Just wife type or mother type, he said. MOREOVER, even meeting him on his own niggardly terms, where did he get this either/ or stuff? What, pray, was to prevent me from being a perfectly peachy blend of *both?* Who, pray, was to say that Miss Peach of 1927 couldn't jolly well be Mrs. Peach of 1949?

Not Dr. O'Whoosis, by a long shot. I guessed I could show him a thing or two with one arm tied behind me. *I'd* pile up a score that would make him sit up and whistle.

The questions were awful easy. It was no strain at all to be truthful and spontaneous. The professor asked silly, easy things like: "If you had an extra five dollars, what would you buy? A new hat for yourself or one for your child?" With only a faint sneer as to what kind of a hat I'd find for five bucks nowadays, I passed on to the next one: "Would you rather curl up with a good novel or read Mother Goose aloud to the baby?" I settled that one in record time and sailed into the next bit of soul-searching: "Are you able (was I able!!) to enjoy an evening out with your husband or do you fret about the children at home?" And the question about whether or not my husband ever had to get his own breakfast made me laugh out loud. Naturally, my husband got his own breakfast. You don't expect a grown man to go to work on an empty stomach, do you?

Well, as I say, the questions were a pip. So was my score. I barely made the grade as a wife and I failed—utterly, dismally—as a mother. Which just goes to show that being analyzed as a peach doesn't guarantee a blamed thing. I think the only reason I skinned through as a wife was because I said I could enjoy a carefree evening out with my husband. This, of course, scored heavily against me as a mother but . . . oh, well, some days you can't make a nickel. But, even allowing for the law of averages, there was no excuse for *anyone* (outside of Dracula or Frankenstein) to flunk motherhood with a score like mine.

"Your score of .008 reveals," announced Dr. O'Whoosis, like the crack of doom, on page 105, "that you have no Mother Instinct."

This was a fine how-do-you-do. They let you go ahead and bear three children and *then* tell you you're not the type. Offhand, I didn't know whether I was supposed to go out and quietly slit my own throat or else drown the three children in the bathtub. Clearly, someone had to get out of the way.

As I tossed on my sleepless cot that night, I tried to cheer myself up by thinking that, at any rate, my children had an *honest* mother. I could have, you know, said I was crazy about reading Mother Goose aloud and no one would have been the wiser. And that hypothetical five bucks I spent on a hat for myself . . . well, gee, maybe I shouldn't have done it but I honestly thought Susie's red felt would get through another winter. Mine was a sight.

I also made medical excuses for myself. I decided, somewhat bitterly, that the Mother Instinct was probably lacking because my three children had all been Caesarian births. There was probably something about having labor pains that turned the trick. Just three days of gas pains didn't count.

With the dawn, though, I began to feel better about Mother Goose and the hat and the gas pains. The situation was still tense but, at least, it explained a lot of my old funny attitudes. It explained, for example, why I have always wanted to snarl and bite at baby photographers. Small wonder. No Mother Instinct to make me joyously respond to their gurgling drivel. ("What a beautiful, beautiful child you have there, Mother. Gitchee-goo, baby, gitchee-goo, Mother. By the way, you'll want at least three gross of these oil-tinted miniatures, won't you, Mother?")

I always thought (somewhat abashed) that I wanted to bite photographers because I had a deficiency of calcium or something in my system. I once read about a woman on a low-calcium diet who had an irresistible urge to bite the shoulder of a certain laundry man. The doctor advised her husband to talk the laundry man into letting her do it. Bad thing, repressions.

Now I saw no particular good reason as to why I, with no Mother

Instinct to hold me back, couldn't let loose and sink my teeth into the very next photographer who gurgled at me. Come to think about it, there were lots of other people I wouldn't mind biting, either. Such as all electrical guitar, tapdancing, baton twirling, and elocution teachers who want to groom my children for MGM, Carnegie Hall, or the Palladium.

Of course, these talent scouts don't start heckling you until the baby is around a year old (I understand they have miniature electrical guitars, infant size) but the ordinary commercial salesmen are on hand

I*

from birth on. Yes, I think that . . . after the photographers and talent scouts . . . I will most enjoy biting salesmen. (Naturally, I intend— thanks to Dr. O'Whoosis—to be an emancipated woman from now on. No more of this secret life of Walter Mitty stuff, just *dreaming* about biting.)

I'm sharpening my fangs for those salesmen who—if you resist their product—make you feel like a monster that eats its young. "You mean," they sneer, "that you intend to go through life without having your child's first shoes immortalized as bronze bookends? You mean you're going to make your baby eat out of a spoon that doesn't have the same design as your own Community Plate? Ugh."

Ah, how it all comes back to me. Everyone told me that my third baby would be Pure Joy ("You won't worry, you'll just enjoy him," they said) but they weren't reckoning on the commercial snakes in my Eden.

I distinctly remember the day I left the maternity ward, two years ago. With my bundle of Pure Joy in my arms, I sat there in a wheelchair waiting for the elevator. Homeward bound. My husband stood beside me, loaded with two pots of hydrangeas, a baby blanket, and my suitcase. Suddenly, a nurse raced frantically down the hall.

"Oh," she exclaimed loudly, so everyone could hear, "don't you want baby's little identification bracelet as a souvenir?" Thanking her for her thoughtfulness, I awkwardly shifted the baby and pocketed a two-inch bead bracelet that spelled out "H-a-s-l-ey." Then, to my horror, I heard her say briskly, "And that'll be one dollar, please."

So, my husband put down the two pots of hydrangeas, the baby blanket, and the suitcase, and dragged out his wallet. It wasn't so much that it left us with just two bus tokens to get home on, understand, but the principle of the thing. With a hospital bill that would choke a horse, couldn't they have tossed that five cent bracelet in for free? A little nosegay to my motherhood? No.

One week home from the hospital, the insurance salesman showed up. Like all loving and far-sighted mothers, I wanted . . . didn't I . . .to prepare for baby's college education? I did, but I also thought it would be sort of nice if we first paid for the baby himself. I'd never forgive myself if the Finance Company came and took Danny away as they did my ironer.

By the time the Elite Studio called, my disposition was getting a little frayed around the edges.

"Is this Mrs. Louis Hasley?" the voice caroled brightly. "*Congratulations!* You have just won a contest! Your name has been selected to receive an 8 x 10 tinted picture of your new baby! When would like your appointment?"

For a split second, I thought Motherhood was going to pay off. I thought I was really going to get something for nothing, but then the bright voice caroled that—whereas the picture was free—obviously there would be a charge for the solid gold frame that went with it. Oh, obviously.

I had about lost my faith in human nature when the Welcome Wagon rolled up to my front curbing. The Welcome Wagon Lady had a market basket full of FREE gifts (all right, *be* crude and call them advertising samples) for me and my babe, all donated by local business men. This touched me to the quick. Just think! Those busy, busy tycoons taking the time to select gifts personally for poor little me. With tears smarting my eyes, I started to relieve the woman of her basket but she wouldn't let go.

It seemed that there was a little ceremony that went with the presentation and I, crude oaf that I was, was rushing the deal. Each little gift, I learned the hard way, was to be slowly and impressively lifted out— accompanied by a sales talk. My part in the ritual (and believe me, all we lacked was some background organ music) was to utter a little cluck of joy and gratitude when she finally handed it over.

I also had to remember directions. For instance, as I received a quart of homogenized milk I was told that the milkman would be around the next morning to collect the empty bottle. He was also very anxious to see how I enjoyed the way the fatty particles were all broken down and how I appreciated the 400 U.S.P. vitamin D units from irradiated ergosterol. Would I have my report ready, please, when he came? (About 6:45 A.M.)

251

Well, it was a bit of a nuisance to swill down the whole quart of milk that evening and prepare my testimonial but . . . there, there, I'm talking like an ingrate. The gifts *were* free and the entire ceremony only took about one and a half hours. I *was* grateful but I decided, just the same, to ask my husband to build a moat around the house to discourage further callers. The after-care of new mothers (I read somewhere) included rest and freedom from anxiety and pressing decisions.

He didn't get the moat built in time, though, to ward off Miss Pinkle, the Super Marvel Book Salesman. Miss Hattie Pinkle, a retired school teacher, caught me with my guard down because I'd caught a bad head cold (lack of rest) and didn't want to stand in the open door.

Unwittingly, I invited her to step inside but as soon as I discovered her mission in life, I began to sneeze and hack—in careless fashion— into my Kleenex. I even mentioned that tuberculosis ran rampant on my mother's side of the family but Miss Pinkle, as I learned to my sorrow, was made of stern stuff. She not only settled down on the davenport but bade me cuddle close to her so that we could look at the Super Marvel Book pictures together.

And beautiful pictures they were, too. Not to mention the valuable and illuminating printed material that went along with them. Did I know what caused lightning? Did I know the different kinds of cloud formation? Could I explain radioactivity? Did I know what makes moss grow on the north side of trees? Could I even explain the rainbow?

No. How then, asked Miss Pinkle (closing in for the kill), was I going to explain it all to my wee one when he asked me?

How, indeed? Wee one's father wasn't any help as Nature Boy; *he* just specialized in Victorian poetry at Notre Dame. But, sitting there bleary-eyed and with a tub of diapers awaiting me in the basement, I couldn't quite get into the spirit of the thing. If I furnished my wee one with dry pants, wasn't that enough? Did he have to complicate things by asking about lightning? But I knew, deep down inside of me, that I was being an unimaginative dolt about the whole affair. Making rapid calculations, I figured that we could (by just living on rice) probably finish paying the last installments on the book by 1964.

Then a horrible thought struck me. If my wee one never asked what made lightning (and *I* wasn't going to bring it up), why . . . why, it would just mean our life savings down the sink. Not to mention getting beriberi from the steady rice diet.

Wouldn't it be far more sensible never to let my wee one see lightning? Lock him in a closet every time it stormed? Or (and this was more constructive), why not give wee one a piece of string and a key and push him out in the storm to discover and harness lightning for himself? After all, no one made things easy for Benjamin Franklin.

So I said, out loud: "No one made it easy for B. Franklin."

Miss Pinkle looked so dazed that, warming to my theme, I launched into the rugged boyhood of Franklin, the Wright Brothers, Robert Fulton, Marconi and Edison. Did they have the Super Marvel Books? Not on your life. Triumphantly, I pointed out that to have such books within easy reach would soften a lad's moral fibre, quench the spark for research, stunt his ingenuity, dull his boyish curiosity at God's natural wonders. . . .

Well, I put in a hard morning's work but Miss Pinkle finally slunk out the front door: dazed, converted, apologetic. The last I heard of her she had given up her shady traffic in worthwhile books and was selling ladies' ready-to-wear in Penny's basement. So I guess I outwitted Miss Pinkle, all right, but look at the time and the energy I had to expend in order to save face. If I had only known *then* what I know *now*—to wit, no Mother Instinct, like an albatross around my neck—I could just have laughed in Miss Pinkle's face.

"Ha," I could have laughed in Miss Pinkle's face, "so you think I'm interested in my own children, eh? Make tracks, Pinkle."

Well, you can see for yourself just how indebted I am to Dr. Albert O'Whoosis for this new freedom. (You can also see for yourself just what the years have done to the little peach in the orchard growing but let's skip lightly over that, shall we?) Actually, I can hardly wait for him to bring out another quiz and let me find out some more about myself.

—From *Reproachfully Yours.*

A GREENER PEACH IN A SMALLER
ORCHARD

A little peach in an orchard grew,
　　Listen to my tale of woe!
A little peach of emerald hue
Warmed by the sun and wet by the dew
It grew, it grew!
　　　　Listen to my tale of woe!
One day in passing the orchard through,
　　Listen to my tale of woe!
That little peach dawned on the view
Of Johnny Jones and his sister Sue,
Them two, them two!
　　　　Listen to my tale of woe!

　　Hard trials for them two,
　　Johnny Jones and his sister Sue,
　　And the peach of emerald hue
　　That grew, that grew,
　　　　Listen to my tale of woe!

Now up at the peach a club they threw,
　　Listen to my tale of woe!
Down from the stem on which it grew,
Fell the little peach of emerald hue.
Poor John! Poor Sue!
　　Listen to my tale of woe!
Now Sue took a bite, and John took a chew,
　　Listen to my tale of woe!
And then the trouble began to brew,
A trouble that the doctor couldn't subdue,
Too true, too true;
　　Listen to my tale of woe!

Under the turf where the daisies grew,
        Listen to my tale of woe!
They planted John and his sister Sue,
And their little souls to the angels flew,
Boo hoo! Boo hoo!
        Listen to my tale of woe!
But what of the peach of emerald hue,
        Listen to my tale of woe!
That was warmed by the sun and wet by the dew?
Ah, well, its mission on earth is through,
Adieu! Adieu!
        Listen to my tale of woe!

Up through the turf where they laid them two,
        Listen to my tale of woe!
There sprang a tree of a kind we knew,
And soon through its branches the zephyrs blew,
A-whoo! A-whoo!
        Listen to my tale of woe!
And upon its trunk where all could view,
        Listen to my tale of woe!
They cut the names of John and Sue,
And "Beware of the peach of emerald hue,
It slew them two!"
        Listen to my tale of woe!

    Hard trials for them two,
    Johnny Jones and his sister Sue,
    And the Peach of emerald hue
    That grew, that grew,
        Listen to my tale of woe!

CONVERSATION PIECES

J. B. MORTON

I

At the Play

HE: Then—

SHE: Yes.

HE: If only I had—ah, but what's the good? You——

SHE: I?

HE: My dear, I had only—

SHE: What's the use? We've—oh, can't you see what this means?

HE: You cannot—darling, you do not—oh, the thing's impossible.

SHE: Ah, don't make it harder for me. Don't you know? Can't you guess?

HE: Sometimes I think that—but, there, it's no good.

SHE: And you ?

HE: What does it matter to you?

SHE: To me?

HE: Or to me? What is it all but frustration and—oh, why was I ever born?

SHE: You—oh, how can one—Ah!

HE: It's true. It's true. It's tru-u-u-ue (*sobbing*).

SHE: My-y-a-a-h! (*breaking down*).

256

II

Over the Tea Table

"Between the Irish drama and the English there is a wide gulf."
(From a speech.)

I have always thought so. But still one might try to combine the two,
thus:

Scene: Mrs. Bolton's Mayfair drawing-room. Tea-time.

MRS. BOLTON: Ah, my dear Mr. Mulcahy—so very, very glad to see you.

MICHAEL MULCAHY: And why wouldn't you, and I walking the roads
of the world, destroyed entirely with the drought. Let you be giving me a bit and a sup, lady of the house, for I'm thinking it's little
comfort there is for an old man, and he raising the keen under the
stars five nights or six, maybe.

MRS. BOLTON: Quite, quite. And how is your dear aunt, may I ask?

MICHAEL: May the divil run away with her soul, the old hag, and she
leppin' along the boreens at the shut of eve like the mad woman
of Drumcondra! Let you not be minding her, lady of the house, for
it's a sore thing to have the clacking tongue. Wirra!

MRS. BOLTON: I beg your pardon——

MICHAEL: I said Wirra! It's a way of ending all this. Now tell me, how
are you and your dear husband?

MRS. BOLTON (*infected*): Is it yourself that's asking, Michael Mulcahy, and he after dying on me four years come Samhain—may
the saints o' God in their golden hats give him comfort, for it's a
good man he was, and kind to the poor.

[We may as well end it here, or it will go on for pages and pages.]

III

We do not Understand

My impression, after visiting one or two of the modern plays, is something like this:

LYDIA: But, my dear, my husband beats me.
JACK: Then come to me. Pack at once. Poor Paula!
DORIS: Who is Paula?
JACK: My wife.
NADINE: My dear Jack, my husband won't beat me.
URSULA: Then leave him. Go to Hugo.
MONICA: Who is Hugo?
VERA: Angela's lover.
SOMEBODY (*in a corner*): Ah, no, no.
PHOEBE: You do not understand.
GLADYS: No man ever understands.
A MAN'S VOICE: You little witch!

IV

More Dialogue

The scene is Mrs. Fiddleborough's drawing-room.

ANTONIA (*Yawning*): So Harry's married already. Ah, well. It's never too early to mend.
JOHN: Yes, but he's such an invisible mender. (*Yawns.*)
ANTONIA: A woman, my dear John, is always—(*shrugs her shoulders*) —a woman.
JOHN: To herself?
ANTONIA: No, to the world.
JOHN: Which world?
ANTONIA (*smiling wisely*): A leading question?

258

JOHN: Leading questions sometimes require leading answers.

ANTONIA: And, very often, misleading answers.

JOHN (*deliberately*): I sometimes think there is no such thing as an answer.

ANTONIA (*wincing*): When a man says that to a woman, he's mortgaging her good will.

JOHN: Yes, but he may be his own bailiff.

ANTONIA: John, when that happens love flies out of the window.

JOHN: And crawls in again by the back-door.

ANTONIA: Supposing it's locked.

JOHN (*triumphantly*): Back-doors are never locked.

[I think that is enough to show you what Mr. Drain can do when he tries.]

V

Perhaps he was Right

THE HIGHBROW: I often think, don't you, that Pater's style is somewhat remote from the essentials of life?

THE NORMAL MAN (*smoking and not understanding a word*): 'M.

THE HIGHBROW: He seems to me to reduce the whole art of writing to——

THE NORMAL MAN: 'M.

THE HIGHBROW: —To a defined code or system, whereby the integral—

THE NORMAL MAN: 'M.

THE HIGHBROW: —Integral denominations are reduced to a minimum of expression.

THE NORMAL MAN: 'M.

THE HIGHBROW: If you take a single one of the more pretentious sentences of Pater, you find—what?

THE NORMAL MAN: 'M.

THE HIGHBROW: Well, what?

THE NORMAL MAN: I haven't the vaguest idea what on earth you are talking about.

VI

My Play

Here is a scene from the first act of my play, of which I spoke recently. Peter and Minette have come back from a dance at 5 a.m. Peter is playing the piano softly, while Minette smokes a cigar dreamily, leaning back in an armchair. Suddenly Minette interrupts the playing.

MINETTE: Peter.

PETER: Yeah.

MINETTE: Oh—I don't know—Peter!

PETER: Um.

MINETTE: It's all so—

PETER (*leaving piano*): I know.

MINETTE: It's so frightfully difficult to be oneself. Peter—

PETER: Ur.

MINETTE: Do you feel that?

PETER: Course I do.

MINETTE (*leaning forward, tense*): I say, how thrilling.

PETER: Ah. (*He rubs champagne behind her ears.*)

MINETTE: Aren't we rotten?

PETER: Rather! To the core!

MINETTE: Why is it?

PETER: One must be something.

MINETTE (*slowly and in awe*): One—must—be—something—(*with a cry*) Peter! I believe that's the solution. That's what's wrong with the world. (*As this is the big speech, she speaks to the audience instead of to Peter.*) We're all too—none of us has the courage to come right out into the open. One—must—be—something. I expect that's what dear old George meant. After all, if we aren't something, what are we? If we could answer that, life would be simple again. Oh, there's too much of everything! Peter, don't you sometimes want to—Oh, you know. Don't you ever say to yourself, "All this is so useless?" Where's it leading? Look at Marjorie. Look at Tom. Look at us. All this—and then—oh, one can't—but one's got to. I reckon it's something or nothing. And here we all are—wasting life, when we might be Being all the time. Being's the thing. One—must—be—something. Oh, Peter, can't we learn from life?

PETER (*serious*): Not unless life learns from us. There's too damn much of it all.

MINETTE (*breaking down and sobbing hysterically*): And it all comes to this! Something! Something! Something!

(CURTAIN)

We now arrive at a very big scene—the one in which Minette, discovered in Scott Houblon's flat by her fifth husband, Walter, explains exactly what it is the modern girl wants. This scene is very advanced, and may make the fathers and mothers wince, but its daring is undeniable, and it faces essentials boldly and bravely.

WALTER: So! It has come to this. We men who lay up to the neck in water on Flanders mud, amid shot and shell, are to be used thus!

MINETTE (*shrilly*): It's your own fault! (*Passionately*) Your own fault, I say! Too long we women have been chattels. After five husbands, I am tired of men, and I have come to Scott for peace.

WALTER: And Scott's wife?

MINETTE: Has fled to Martin.

WALTER: And Martin?

MINETTE: Is with Myra. He has the courage of his convictions, Walter. Listen to me. I am a human being, with an individuality of my own, and I am only doing what everybody is doing now. You are Victorian. You would like me to wear a long dress and ringlets. That's all over, Walter. What is home to me? What was it ever to me? A place where I had a husband and food and drink and friends and books. Was I to be satisfied with that? Was I to sit and moult, while I might be—might be here in this flat? Scott understands,

Scott—
(Enter SCOTT *with* MARJORIE.*)*

WALTER: Marjorie! My wife!

MINETTE: Scott! *(To* WALTER*)* And is Marjorie your wife, too?

*(*WALTER *hangs his head.)*

SCOTT: Minette, it's no good. You taught me how to express myself. I had to be myself.

WALTER: And am I to stand by and lose both of you?

MARJORIE: It was your fault, Walter. You never understood.

(The telephone rings.)

MINETTE: Yes! Yes! It's Minette. Yes! Oh, my darling! Oh, Edgar! Yes, at once. I'm coming to you now!

(Exit)

MARJORIE: I never trusted Edgar.

*(*CURTAIN*)*

—From *By the Way.*

262

NEBUCHADNEZZAR

Whom Catholics usually call Nabuchodonosor.

G. K. CHESTERTON

Nebuchadnezzar, the King of the Jews,
Suffered from new and original views,
He crawled on his hands and knees it's said,
With grass in his mouth and a crown on his head.

Those in traditional paths that trod,
Thought the thing was a curse from God;
But a Pioneer men always abuse,
Like Nebuchadnezzar the King of the Jews.

Black Lord Foulon the Frenchmen slew,
Thought it a Futurist thing to do;
He offered them grass instead of bread,
So they stuffed him with grass when they cut off his head.

For the pride of his soul he perished then,
But of course it is always of Pride that men
A Man in Advance of his Age accuse
Like Nebuchadnezzar the King of the Jews.

Simeon Scudder of Styx, in Maine,
Thought of the thing and was at it again;
He gave good grass and water in pails
To a thousand Irishmen hammering rails,

Appetites differ, and tied to a stake,
He was tarred and feathered for Conscience Sake;
But stoning the prophets is ancient news,
Like Nebuchadnezzar the King of the Jews.

—From *The Flying Inn.*

THE GHOSTS OF BESFORD COURT

MGR. THOMAS NEWSOME

The only ghost I have ever seen at Besford or indeed in my whole life, although I have had experiences in another haunted house, was an "elemental." These are described profusely in psychic literature. An elemental is first cousin to a poltergeist, which is a thing like a mischievous schoolboy gone mad and which hurls objects about and sometimes injures human beings.

Our elemental is round about the Dower House and only at very rare intervals makes its presence seen. Many years ago my stepsister, Mrs. Brown, was gravely injured in a motor accident and her mother came to look after her. Both slept in the room in the Dower House in the southeast corner. Mr. Webb happened to be staying the night, and we both went to bed early. This is the story I heard next morning. My stepmother knocked at my door, but knocked so gently that she failed to rouse me. Consequently she went to Mr. Webb's room and knocked on his door and he awoke immediately. She explained to him there was a big light in the study, that it was streaming across the lawn and lighting up the trunk and lower branches of the beech tree on the edge of the further lawn.

At that time our principal sources of illumination were two candelabra, each carrying three candles. We took them in to our evening meal and we brought them back into the study. That night as usual we had blown them out and taken our bedroom candles to light us to bed. Where was the light coming from? Mr. Webb said he would get up and look. Asking my stepmother to stand at the top of the stairs in case anyone tried to get upstairs, he went down very circumspectly to the study door. He soon returned saying there was no light in the study and that he had looked through the keyhole. My stepmother went back to her bedroom and she and Mrs. Brown saw that the light was still streaming out from the windows. After about five minutes it suddenly vanished. Next day on hearing the story I invited them all to examine the door of the study. There was no keyhole.

About a year later two visitors were sitting in front of the fire, the six candles being alight in the centre of the table. They both saw a dense black shadow, with the outline of a woman with a headgear something like that of a nun, pass slowly across the whitewashed wall above the fireplace. This shadow could not have come from the candles, which were stationary, or from the fire, which is immediately under the sha-

dow; neither could it have been cast by either of the two sitting figures or from anything else in the room.

About three years later it was reported to me that a queer, unearthly face had been seen pressed against a window in the kitchen and that on noticing that it was observed it had withdrawn and disappeared. I attached no importance to this, but about four years later I myself went into the lowest lavatory and saw at a distance of about two feet a hypoplastic face looking at me—the eyes were round and opened wide, the nose was a lump, and the mouth a line, the face itself was round. We looked at one another for about twenty seconds and the face then slowly receded. It corresponds with the face of what is known as an elemental.

It must be remembered that the site of Besford Court and its immediate environment has on account of its natural advantages been the centre of human life for many thousands of years. There was a great house there at the time of the Norman Conquest. The early Anglo-Saxons were here, as we know from the graveyard in which their skeletons were found. The Romans had a station here and the ramparts of their stockaded camp still exist in the Roman Field. A site that appealed to them would appeal to earlier settlers, and the fertile vale of Evesham must have made a good place of settlement to the Paleolithic men.

Things and influences linger on in spite of Christianity in these ancient abodes of the human race. Concentrations of humanity together acting as spiritual forces tend either to wipe them out or else to irritate them into making final efforts. We are immersed in a world of unseen realities. To me, it is marvellous how seldom the barriers of the two worlds are broken down.

—From *Shane Leslie's Ghost Book.*

YOU'RE VERY WELCOME

Hostess: And now make yourselves at home, where I wish you were.

INDEX OF AUTHORS